Wordpuzzler Book

C	H	E	S	S	M	O	V	I	S
A	E	W	L	L	A	K	L	X	N
M	Y	F	A	I	R	L	A	D	Y
E	N	E	I	V	Y	A	M	G	D
L	T	V	S	R	L	H	A	I	R
O	L	I	V	E	R	O	L	G	I
T	V	T	E	L	O	M	N	I	N
O	C	A	T	S	J	A	G	R	S
K	E	D	K	T	O	G	A	B	L
Y	R	S	H	O	W	B	O	A	T

The names of 10 famous musicals are hidden in the grid. To help you find them, we've given you a song from each.

THE SONGS

1. I Remember It Well
2. How To Handle A Woman
3. The Rain In Spain
4. Consider Yourself
5. Aquarius
6. Memory
7. Oh What A Beautiful Morning
8. Old Man River
9. I Know Him So Well
10. Don't Cry For Me Argentina

2

T	S	P	S	Q	D	U	M	A	S
X	O	L	W	I	N	F	E	U	R
P	A	D	I	C	K	E	N	S	T
E	V	I	F	N	E	S	G	T	I
P	E	L	T	O	L	K	I	E	N
D	R	Y	H	R	A	A	L	N	G
A	N	N	S	W	R	C	H	A	P
D	E	F	O	E	T	U	U	G	E
E	A	A	L	L	Y	S	G	I	N
B	R	T	O	L	S	T	O	Y	S

The names of 10 world-famous authors are hidden in our word grid. To help you identify them we've given you the title of a novel written by each.

1. War and Peace
2. The Lord of the Rings
3. Robinson Crusoe
4. Gullivers Travels
5. Les Miserables
6. The Three Musketeers
7. Pride and Prejudice
8. 1984
9. David Copperfield
10. Around the World in 80 Days

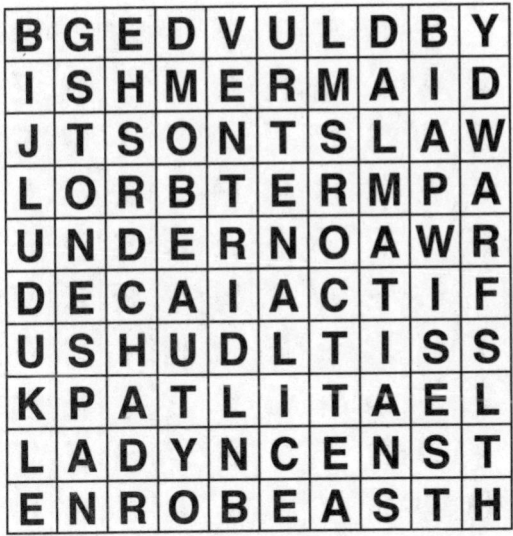

B	G	E	D	V	U	L	D	B	Y
I	S	H	M	E	R	M	A	I	D
J	T	S	O	N	T	S	L	A	W
L	O	R	B	T	E	R	M	P	A
U	N	D	E	R	N	O	A	W	R
D	E	C	A	I	A	C	T	I	F
U	S	H	U	D	L	T	I	S	S
K	P	A	T	L	I	T	A	E	L
L	A	D	Y	N	C	E	N	S	T
E	N	R	O	B	E	A	S	T	H

HERE are 10 titles of famous
Walt Disney films. Can you find
the missing words in our grid?

1. ---- and the Tramp
2. The Rescuers Down -----
3. Peter ---
4. Snow White and the Seven
   ------
5. The Little --------
6. Sleeping ------
7. The Sword in the -----
8. One Hundred and One
   ----
9. Beauty and the -----
10. ----- in Wonderland

4

L	E	N	S	T	Y	T	W	A	R
V	I	L	G	E	O	B	S	R	E
E	W	S	P	N	N	F	I	V	E
L	E	R	S	C	H	I	X	O	L
F	I	F	T	E	E	N	S	P	E
I	G	E	W	T	H	I	H	K	V
T	H	R	E	E	D	N	I	C	E
F	T	O	N	O	S	E	V	E	N
Y	U	R	T	F	R	P	H	E	T
S	W	S	Y	T	I	A	C	R	O

WE have 10 numbers hidden in the wordsquare. Solve the clues and find the words.

1. Number in a score
2. How many players in a soccer team?
3. --- wives of Henry VIII
4. --- Commandments
5. How many in a rugby union team?
6. ------ Deadly Sins
7. A cat has ---- lives
8. The ------ Wise Men
9. How many furlongs in a mile?
10. Number of rings on the Olympic flag

H	G	A	K	E	R	S	M	I	G
A	S	K	I	N	W	U	L	T	U
S	T	N	D	O	R	M	E	J	M
J	O	I	N	T	O	M	P	A	S
E	M	P	E	X	D	E	A	R	P
P	A	L	Y	O	T	Y	R	E	N
A	C	H	E	N	N	E	R	V	E
T	H	I	R	L	O	O	P	G	H
R	E	M	J	C	S	S	W	Q	I
K	O	L	I	V	E	R	Y	N	O

HOW are you feeling today? To cheer you up, we've a list of ailments. Each 'itis listed affects a different part of the body and they're all hidden in the wordsquare. Words are written horizontally and vertically.

1. HEPATITIS
2. ARTHRITIS
3. GASTRITIS
4. NEURITIS
5. RHINITIS
6. DERMATITIS
7. OTITIS
8. NEPHRITIS
9. GINGIVITIS
10. CONJUNCTIVITIS

6

A	K	E	N	T	O	T	W	A	C
G	E	R	E	P	C	R	A	C	O
G	L	O	W	S	B	I	R	O	O
A	L	I	M	N	O	G	E	R	P
B	Y	G	A	N	G	A	B	L	E
L	R	U	N	P	A	R	M	O	R
P	E	R	D	B	R	A	N	D	O
E	F	F	O	A	T	N	E	E	D
G	R	A	N	T	E	I	N	A	G
E	S	U	N	S	W	A	Y	N	E

OUR word puzzle is hiding the surnames of 10 famous actors. To help you find them we've given a list of films in which they starred.

1. The Hustler
2. On the Waterfront
3. Singin' in the Rain
4. Rebel Without a Cause
5. High Noon
6. Casablanca
7. North by Northwest
8. Gone With the Wind
9. True Grit
10. Pretty Woman

A	G	O	N	D	O	L	A	S	T
T	T	V	E	I	B	V	C	O	G
T	R	A	M	P	R	A	C	E	R
G	I	N	A	P	P	L	A	N	E
A	C	H	E	T	R	U	B	L	Y
S	K	A	C	A	M	E	L	I	H
U	S	T	E	X	O	N	E	R	O
C	H	R	O	I	M	P	C	J	U
R	A	F	T	E	T	R	A	I	N
E	W	G	A	R	T	Y	R	O	D

THE clues listed below describe different forms of transport.
Can you find the answers in our grid?

1. Car hired with driver
2. American long-distance bus
3. Road transport vehicle running on tracks
4. Ship of the desert
5. Floating platform
6. Flying vehicle, commonly
7. Asian man-drawn passenger vehicle
8. Locomotive-drawn line of carriages
9. Venetian canal taxi
10. Suspended cabin for reaching mountain peaks

8

R	I	N	C	A	I	R	O	N	W
O	S	L	O	U	T	H	R	L	I
S	O	P	P	L	A	M	M	A	N
T	F	R	E	D	L	O	N	G	T
E	I	I	N	B	O	U	T	O	F
B	A	T	H	E	N	S	I	S	E
S	Q	U	A	L	M	E	X	H	E
I	M	T	G	L	O	O	K	E	S
N	E	A	E	T	R	U	J	L	T
B	E	R	N	I	E	L	I	M	A

CAN you identify the capitals of the countries listed below. Answers are in our wordsquare and are listed horizontally and vertically, but not backwards or diagonally.

1. SWITZERLAND
2. PERU
3. GREECE
4. SOUTH KOREA
5. DENMARK
6. NIGERIA
7. BULGARIA
8. NORWAY
9. JORDAN
10. EGYPT

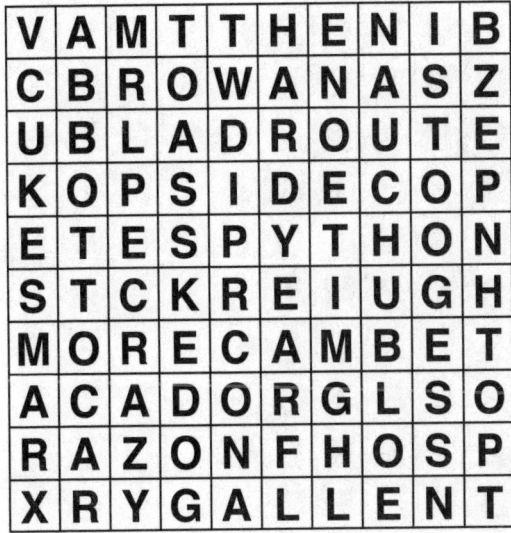

V	A	M	T	T	H	E	N	I	B
C	B	R	O	W	A	N	A	S	Z
U	B	L	A	D	R	O	U	T	E
K	O	P	S	I	D	E	C	O	P
E	T	E	S	P	Y	T	H	O	N
S	T	C	K	R	E	I	U	G	H
M	O	R	E	C	A	M	B	E	T
A	C	A	D	O	R	G	L	S	O
R	A	Z	O	N	F	H	O	S	P
X	R	Y	G	A	L	L	E	N	T

THERE are the names of 10 comedy teams or partnerships hidden in our grid. See if you can find the missing words from the clues below.

1. Laurel and -----
2. The Keystone ----
3. ---------- and Wise
4. The Three --------
5. The ----- Gang
6. ----- and Martin
7. Monty ------'s Flying Circus
8. Flanagan and -----
9. The ---- Brothers
10. ----- and Costello

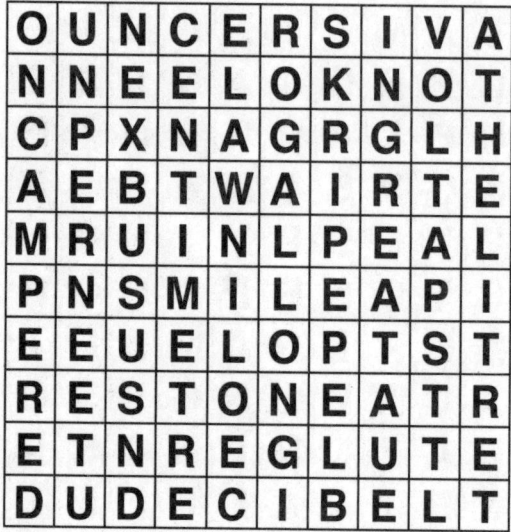

O	U	N	C	E	R	S	I	V	A
N	N	E	E	L	O	K	N	O	T
C	P	X	N	A	G	R	G	L	H
A	E	B	T	W	A	I	R	T	E
M	R	U	I	N	L	P	E	A	L
P	N	S	M	I	L	E	A	P	I
E	E	U	E	L	O	P	T	S	T
R	E	S	T	O	N	E	A	T	R
E	T	N	R	E	G	L	U	T	E
D	U	D	E	C	I	B	E	L	T

WEIGHTS and measures is our theme. See if you can find the answers in the grid.

1. Unit of electrical potential
2. Eight furlongs
3. 1 cubic decimetre
4. One sixteenth of a pound
5. Unit of electrical current
6. 10 millimetres
7. 1 nautical mile per hour
8. Eight pints
9. Unit of sound
10. 14lbs

T	S	U	G	A	R	C	A	N	E
M	I	N	O	N	B	I	W	R	G
T	R	E	S	I	N	G	L	O	G
R	U	D	L	S	T	H	A	J	R
I	P	A	W	E	B	E	R	U	I
P	E	P	P	E	R	M	I	N	T
L	S	P	U	D	I	C	X	I	H
U	B	L	I	N	G	R	A	P	E
M	E	E	D	O	G	A	V	E	N
P	U	D	U	C	H	E	R	R	Y

YOU'LL get tipsy on this puzzle. We've given you the drink, can you find a main ingredient of that drink in our grid?

1. CALVADOS
2. KIRSCH
3. RETSINA
4. OUZO
5. GIN
6. ADVOCAAT
7. CREME DE MENTHE
8. SLIVOVITZ
9. RUM
10. GRAPPA

E	D	U	S	B	R	O	W	N	S
N	I	J	P	R	E	A	Y	K	O
D	G	R	U	N	D	R	A	B	L
M	G	O	R	B	I	N	B	U	F
T	R	I	P	P	A	B	L	U	E
Y	E	L	L	O	W	N	A	R	M
H	Y	P	E	S	H	O	C	I	N
T	E	E	S	P	I	N	K	L	I
O	G	R	M	O	T	H	I	L	L
L	O	G	R	E	E	N	T	H	E

COLOUR is the theme of this puzzle. Try to find the missing words in our grid.

1. ----- with envy
2. ---- matter; brains
3. ------ streak; cowardly trait
4. Feeling ----; to be depressed
5. Seeing ---; angry
6. ------ prose, fanciful or elaborate writing
7. -----ed off; to be disheartened
8. In the ----; healthy
9. In the -----; in credit
10. ----- flag; surrender

G	I	L	T	U	P	P	S	E	T
O	N	U	S	N	O	O	K	E	R
L	Y	C	A	L	L	O	I	D	U
F	C	R	G	R	O	W	I	N	G
R	H	I	T	O	V	I	N	I	B
Y	A	C	H	T	I	N	G	L	Y
I	R	K	T	E	P	P	E	X	E
S	T	E	N	N	I	S	M	P	A
O	R	T	I	D	W	D	O	V	R
B	E	S	O	S	O	C	C	E	R

FEELING sporty? This word puzzle is all about sports and sporting venues. We've listed the venue, see if you can find the sport in the grid. Words are written horizontally and vertically, but not diagonally or backwards.

1. **VAL D'ISERE**
2. **HENLEY**
3. **LORD'S**
4. **COWDRAY PARK**
5. **ST ANDREW'S**
6. **TWICKENHAM**
7. **COWES**
8. **ANFIELD**
9. **CRUCIBLE THEATRE**
10. **WIMBLEDON**

B	Z	R	U	F	L	E	D	F	S
J	E	A	N	O	H	E	N	R	Y
H	A	R	I	L	A	J	O	A	L
E	R	I	K	R	T	L	O	N	E
L	U	G	L	A	T	R	A	Z	D
U	W	O	L	F	G	A	N	G	W
D	H	R	P	E	J	L	S	T	A
W	O	P	P	L	R	P	O	S	R
I	V	E	R	I	C	H	A	R	D
G	I	N	O	X	M	A	S	A	X

CAN you put the right first names to the classical composers listed below? The names are hidden in the grid, written horizontally and vertically, but not diagonally or backwards.

1. Mendelssohn
2. Sibelius
3. Purcell
4. Wagner
5. Stravinsky
6. Schubert
7. Mozart
8. Elgar
9. Vaughan-Williams
10. Beethoven

S	T	E	G	P	A	I	M	S	O
C	L	A	R	A	B	B	I	T	E
A	E	S	E	R	L	T	S	O	M
T	I	G	E	R	M	H	E	A	P
E	T	L	M	O	T	O	L	D	E
R	H	O	T	T	E	R	M	A	L
T	R	R	D	E	N	S	H	E	D
R	A	G	O	O	S	E	N	D	O
E	N	U	M	O	U	S	P	I	G
T	O	M	I	P	E	P	E	N	E

THERE are 10 literary animals listed in our puzzle grid this week. We've given you the animal's name, you must find the type of animal.

1. Tarka the -----
2. Peter -------
3. J M Barrie's Nana
4. Black Beauty
5. George Orwell's Napoleon
6. ----- of ----- Hall.
7. Robert Louis Stevenson's Captain Flint
8. Kipling's Shere Khan
9. The Snow -----
10. Macavity the ---

P	A	R	I	S	S	R	E	T	M
S	T	O	W	I	T	O	K	Y	O
H	E	V	A	B	I	D	U	P	N
E	R	O	D	E	Y	E	L	A	T
L	I	C	H	R	O	M	E	L	R
S	E	O	U	L	D	O	R	A	E
I	N	M	A	I	R	S	C	A	A
N	O	M	U	N	I	C	H	Y	L
K	I	T	R	G	F	O	E	G	A
I	G	I	A	N	T	W	E	R	P

FEELING sporty, this is just your game. We've given you a year and a gold medal winner from 10 Olympic games. You have to find the venues.

1. 1960: Cassius Clay
2. 1980: Duncan Goodhew
3. 1952: Emil Zatopek
4. 1976: Lasse Viren
5. 1936: Jesse Owens
6. 1920: Albert Hill
7. 1988: Adrian Moorhouse
8. 1964: Lynn Davies
9. 1924: Johnny Weissmuller
10.1972: Mary Peters

O	R	C	O	M	I	S	R	E	B
B	E	O	G	O	R	M	O	O	A
E	X	P	I	S	A	N	M	T	T
R	H	E	N	C	L	E	E	S	H
L	O	N	D	O	N	T	N	E	E
I	R	H	I	W	E	E	L	T	N
N	E	A	P	N	P	A	R	I	S
E	A	G	R	A	M	N	I	H	O
R	I	E	L	A	S	T	B	U	V
W	A	N	E	W	Y	O	R	K	A

TEN famous landmarks are listed. Can you find the cities where they are sited in our word grid? Words are written horizontally and vertically, not diagonally or backwards.

1. Eiffel Tower
2. Little Mermaid
3. Parthenon
4. Brandenburg Gate
5. Marble Arch
6. Leaning Tower
7. Taj Mahal
8. Statue of Liberty
9. Colosseum
10. Kremlin

L	I	N	K	I	D	L	O	S	T
F	M	U	I	M	P	E	R	C	H
O	A	R	T	I	R	U	P	U	P
A	V	O	T	T	A	R	I	B	I
L	E	V	E	R	E	T	I	A	L
A	R	I	N	E	S	S	P	F	O
B	L	G	T	H	M	C	H	A	R
O	A	L	A	J	O	A	S	W	S
L	M	E	G	O	S	L	I	N	G
E	B	R	O	R	T	F	L	O	N

A YOUNG cat is called a kitten, but do you know the name for a young hare? We've given you 10 animals, can you find their young in our wordsquare?

1. ELEPHANT
2. CAT
3. SHEEP
4. DEER
5. GOAT
6. GOOSE
7. HARE
8. SEAL
9. HORSE
10. FOX

D	R	U	M	S	A	V	E	S	T
O	E	G	I	T	S	I	T	A	R
H	A	R	P	O	L	O	A	X	E
S	P	L	A	C	E	L	L	O	W
D	U	G	N	K	W	I	S	P	H
F	L	U	T	E	R	N	C	H	O
B	L	I	I	N	E	T	H	O	M
L	E	T	R	A	P	I	A	N	O
S	C	A	O	L	U	Z	R	E	T
I	T	R	U	M	P	E	T	E	R

CAN you identify the instruments associated with the musicians listed below? Words are written horizontally and vertically, not diagonally or backwards.

1. James Galway
2. Buddy Rich
3. Johnny Dankworth
4. Mary O'Hara
5. Elton John
6. Stéphane Grappelli
7. Eric Clapton
8. Pablo Casals
9. Miles Davis
10. Ravi Shankar

T	A	S	T	I	C	L	S	I	T
A	S	K	U	L	L	Y	C	R	I
S	U	R	B	I	A	P	A	L	B
C	R	I	B	L	V	A	P	R	I
V	E	B	I	F	I	B	U	L	A
L	S	U	S	H	C	E	L	I	B
M	P	A	T	E	L	L	A	X	T
E	I	N	E	J	E	G	R	J	I
R	N	I	R	U	W	R	E	A	D
F	E	M	U	R	D	E	N	W	O

THEM bones, them bones... Can you find the medical names for these bones? Words are written horizontally and vertically, but not diagonally or backwards.

1. Shoulder blade
2. Backbone
3. Chest bone
4. Shin bone
5. Collarbone
6. Chin bone
7. Kneecap
8. Thigh bone
9. Head bone
10. Outer leg bone

R	E	A	R	H	O	N	E	S	A
H	R	B	T	O	R	E	D	A	C
I	G	O	R	L	N	R	O	Y	L
N	A	N	O	L	I	F	F	E	Y
E	N	C	D	I	L	M	N	V	D
X	T	H	A	M	E	S	T	I	E
F	I	R	N	U	N	G	L	E	C
N	B	O	U	R	S	E	I	N	E
G	E	L	B	E	N	G	N	T	N
P	R	E	E	S	T	R	I	O	K

THE cities listed all have famous rivers running through them. The rivers are hidden in our word grid. Can you find all 10? Words are written horizontally and vertically, not diagonally or backwards.

1. Vienna
2. Paris
3. Glasgow
4. Rotterdam
5. London
6. Hamburg
7. Dublin
8. Rome
9. Geneva
10. Cairo

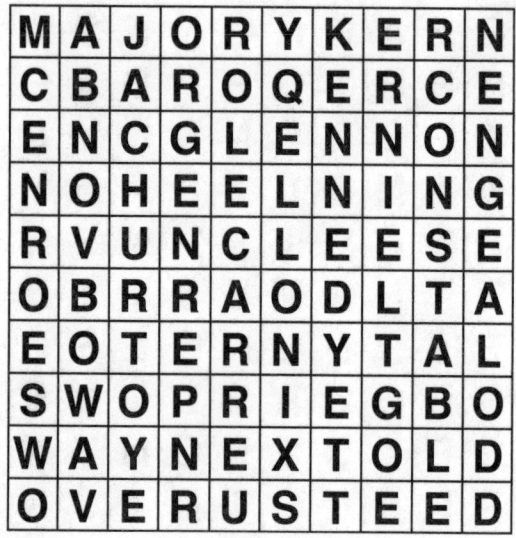

M	A	J	O	R	Y	K	E	R	N
C	B	A	R	O	Q	E	R	C	E
E	N	C	G	L	E	N	N	O	N
N	O	H	E	E	L	N	I	N	G
R	V	U	N	C	L	E	E	S	E
O	B	R	R	A	O	D	L	T	A
E	O	T	E	R	N	Y	T	A	L
S	W	O	P	R	I	E	G	B	O
W	A	Y	N	E	X	T	O	L	D
O	V	E	R	U	S	T	E	E	D

THERE are a lot of famous Johns. Can you guess their surnames and find them in the word grid?

1. Oscar-winning actor in True Grit
2. Former British Prime Minister
3. Three times Wimbledon champion
4. Star of the film A Fish Called Wanda
5. Painted The Hay Wain
6. US President assassinated in 1963
7. Character played by Patrick MacNee in The Avengers
8. Author of Tinker, Tailor, Soldier, Spy
9. Actor in The Elephant Man
10. One of The Beatles

I	O	A	W	Y	M	O	I	N	G
L	O	U	I	S	I	A	N	A	E
L	I	T	L	E	C	L	E	D	F
I	T	A	K	A	H	O	V	I	L
N	E	H	W	H	I	D	A	H	O
O	X	E	M	A	G	E	D	A	R
I	S	O	A	H	A	W	A	I	I
S	A	H	T	O	N	A	M	N	D
O	V	I	Y	M	O	N	A	T	A
Y	C	O	L	O	R	A	D	O	T

CAN you match these American cities with the states they are in? Words are written horizontally and vertically, not diagonally or backwards.

1. Salt Lake City
2. Miami
3. Denver
4. Detroit
5. Boise
6. Honolulu
7. Chicago
8. Cleveland
9. New Orleans
10. Las Vegas

E	S	H	W	A	M	A	B	E	R
S	P	I	E	L	B	E	R	G	A
C	A	T	L	L	E	B	O	G	D
O	S	C	S	E	R	F	O	R	D
R	I	H	L	N	R	G	K	I	E
S	R	C	E	R	C	A	S	O	R
E	N	O	S	K	A	R	A	L	B
S	A	C	O	P	P	O	L	A	I
E	N	K	I	R	R	W	I	N	N
S	L	E	L	E	A	N	A	G	L

CAN you say who directed these 10 famous films?

1. The Godfather: Francis Ford --------
2. Psycho: Alfred ----------
3. Metropolis: Fritz ----
4. Stagecoach: John ----
5. Taxi Driver: Martin --------
6. Lawrence of Arabia: David ------------
7. ET: Steven ----------
8. Blazing Saddles: Mel ------
9. Annie Hall: Woody -----
10. Arsenic and Old Lace: Frank -----

G	R	U	B	Y	E	N	C	R	I
O	I	R	R	A	X	T	H	U	R
R	O	S	A	P	P	H	I	R	E
C	L	A	M	P	A	S	N	I	G
R	A	G	R	A	P	E	A	R	L
Y	R	O	U	T	E	A	P	L	O
S	I	L	V	E	R	Y	L	O	W
T	A	D	P	O	C	A	J	U	O
A	T	E	O	L	H	R	V	E	O
L	A	R	D	I	A	M	O	N	D

CAN you identify what substances are associated with these wedding anniversaries? Words are written horizontally and vertically, not diagonally or backwards.

CLUES

1. 60th
2. 40th
3. 15th
4. 50th
5. 30th
6. 5th
7. 20th
8. 45th
9. 2nd
10. 25th

C	P	H	I	L	I	P	H	I	S
L	E	A	C	O	R	G	E	F	U
E	T	R	C	H	A	R	L	E	S
M	S	Q	U	I	D	G	I	R	A
I	A	L	I	C	E	L	Z	G	R
C	N	O	R	M	D	I	A	N	A
A	N	D	R	E	W	I	B	D	H
H	E	L	A	Z	A	R	E	R	O
M	A	R	G	A	R	E	T	E	W
L	R	I	C	H	D	A	H	R	A

CAN you identify the first names of the royals listed? Words are written horizontally and vertically, not diagonally or backwards.

1. Duke of York
2. Duchess of York
3. Prince of Wales
4. The late Princess of Wales
5. The late Queen Mother
6. Duke of Edinburgh
7. Duke of Kent
8. The former Duchess of Gloucester, aunt to the Queen
9. Princess Royal
10. The late Countess of Snowdon

A	L	B	D	A	N	C	E	R	B
L	G	A	E	G	E	A	N	U	L
B	U	N	A	A	G	R	O	R	A
A	Z	A	D	R	I	A	T	I	C
L	N	L	R	O	D	B	I	A	K
T	I	R	E	D	R	I	A	N	E
I	R	E	S	T	E	A	N	O	R
C	A	S	P	I	A	N	O	R	E
E	L	I	U	H	L	A	P	T	T
D	T	A	S	M	A	N	S	H	Y

THE two countries listed in each clue have borders on a particular sea. Can you find those seas in our wordgrid? Words are written horizontally and vertically only.

1. Poland and Sweden
2. Turkey and Ukraine
3. England and Denmark
4. Italy and Albania
5. Australia and New Zealand
6. Israel and Jordan
7. Iran and Russia
8. Greece and Turkey
9. Egypt and Saudi Arabia
10. India and Oman

S	U	C	R	E	E	F	P	N	U
T	R	I	A	N	G	L	E	I	S
O	D	R	Y	C	R	U	N	J	P
P	O	C	D	A	S	G	T	H	H
Y	E	L	O	S	Q	U	A	R	E
R	W	E	H	P	R	N	G	E	R
A	N	D	M	I	S	C	O	N	E
M	R	U	K	R	I	L	N	A	T
I	M	P	L	A	N	E	T	R	I
D	I	P	U	L	S	C	U	B	E

THE clues below describe geometric figures.
Can you find them in our wordgrid?

1. A four-sided figure
2. A globe
3. A three-sided figure
4. A solid with a square base and triangular sides
5. A solid with six square faces
6. A five-sided figure
7. Perfectly round two dimensional figure
8. Solid with a circular base that tapers to a point
9. A flat surface
10. A helix

R	D	I	E	T	R	I	C	H	A
O	R	I	V	A	N	A	M	E	L
B	R	D	A	Y	A	G	N	T	E
A	U	R	A	L	W	A	S	H	N
C	L	E	M	O	N	R	O	E	X
A	A	B	O	R	I	L	U	P	H
L	S	I	R	D	G	A	R	B	O
L	E	I	G	H	T	N	O	U	R
E	L	G	A	O	E	D	P	R	U
O	F	O	N	D	A	R	I	N	G

CAN you find the female stars of the films listed? To help you, we've given their first names.

1. The African Queen: Katharine (7)
2. The Big Sleep: Lauren (6)
3. Barbarella: Jane (5)
4. Cleopatra: Elizabeth (6)
5. Gone With the Wind: Vivien (5)
6. The Blue Angel: Marlene (8)
7. The Wizard of Oz: Judy (7)
8. The Seven Year Itch: Marilyn (6)
9. Calamity Jane: Doris (3)
10. Ninotchka: Greta (5)

B	R	O	A	D	W	A	Y	R	S
E	A	M	G	R	O	V	L	A	T
W	V	A	D	I	A	R	O	D	R
A	E	R	U	V	D	I	T	C	E
L	N	C	R	E	S	C	E	N	T
K	U	L	H	I	L	W	R	V	E
T	B	O	U	L	V	A	R	D	M
R	I	S	E	O	P	L	A	C	E
E	V	E	N	U	R	Y	C	I	W
T	R	U	G	A	R	D	E	N	S

THERE are many different types of road, but some have names which have another meaning.

1. To put in position (5)
2. An increase in salary (4)
3. A cat's cries (4)
4. A golf shot (5)
5. Horticultural areas (7)
6. A row of houses (7)
7. New York theatreland (8)
8. Hot and humid (5)
9. To ambulate (4)
10. Emblem of Islam (8)

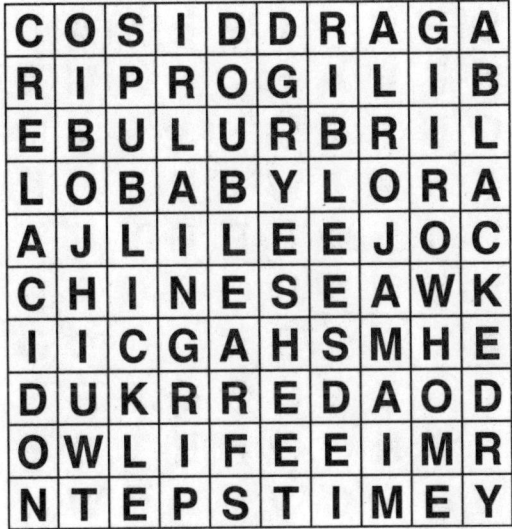

C	O	S	I	D	D	R	A	G	A
R	I	P	R	O	G	I	L	I	B
E	B	U	L	U	R	B	R	I	L
L	O	B	A	B	Y	L	O	R	A
A	J	L	I	L	E	E	J	O	C
C	H	I	N	E	S	E	A	W	K
I	I	C	G	A	H	S	M	H	E
D	U	K	R	R	E	D	A	O	D
O	W	L	I	F	E	E	I	M	R
N	T	E	P	S	T	I	M	E	Y

THE three words in each clue can all follow another word, which you need to find in the grid.

1. ------ house, school, enemy
2. ---- run, guard, rule
3. ---- insurance, style, raft
4. ------ cross, bass, fault
5. ---- drop, test, rain
6. ----- belt, pudding, widow
7. -------- lantern, chequers, whispers
8. ----- metal, lightning, music
9. ---- limit, bomb, warp
10. ---- talk, boom, grand

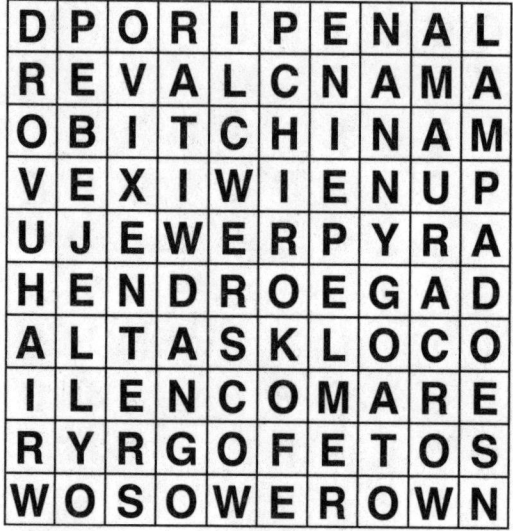

D	P	O	R	I	P	E	N	A	L
R	E	V	A	L	C	N	A	M	A
O	B	I	T	C	H	I	N	A	M
V	E	X	I	W	I	E	N	U	P
U	J	E	W	E	R	P	Y	R	A
H	E	N	D	R	O	E	G	A	D
A	L	T	A	S	K	L	O	C	O
I	L	E	N	C	O	M	A	R	E
R	Y	R	G	O	F	E	T	O	S
W	O	S	O	W	E	R	O	W	N

LISTED here are 10 male animals. Can you find their female counterparts in our word grid?

1. Ram
2. Stallion
3. Cock
4. Bull
5. Billy goat
6. Dog
7. Fox
8. Boar
9. Buck
10. Cob

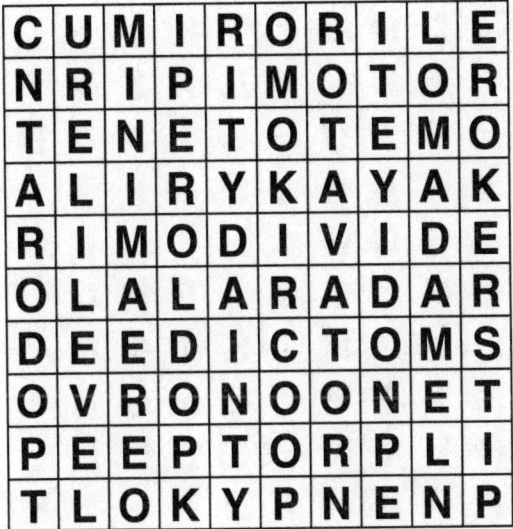

C	U	M	I	R	O	R	I	L	E
N	R	I	P	I	M	O	T	O	R
T	E	N	E	T	O	T	E	M	O
A	L	I	R	Y	K	A	Y	A	K
R	I	M	O	D	I	V	I	D	E
O	L	A	L	A	R	A	D	A	R
D	E	E	D	I	C	T	O	M	S
O	V	R	O	N	O	O	N	E	T
P	E	E	P	T	O	R	P	L	I
T	L	O	K	Y	P	N	E	N	P

THE clues listed here all signify a word which is the same written forwards and backwards. They are all hidden in our wordsearch grid can you find them?

1. Midday
2. Lady's term of respect
3. Principle
4. Action
5. Type of canoe
6. Even
7. Note value
8. Garden digger
9. Look furtively
10. Navigation aid

T	D	O	L	L	Y	M	U	R	L
H	A	R	D	Y	C	A	S	N	E
R	R	B	U	S	U	P	N	U	B
I	K	A	C	L	O	S	E	T	I
B	S	C	K	I	R	E	T	L	G
O	R	H	I	T	I	P	H	O	H
S	H	O	R	T	S	I	I	B	T
M	I	T	R	L	O	N	G	A	T
O	F	I	N	E	L	O	H	B	E
A	F	A	R	I	S	I	S	S	K

FIND the missing word in our grid and complete the film title.

1. ----- Encounters of the Third Kind
2. ---- Noon
3. --- and Away
4. ----- Circuit
5. ------ Big Man
6. The ---- Crystal
7. The ---- Good Friday
8. Some Like it ---
9. A ---- Day's Night
10. The --- Sleep

S	L	I	S	P	I	N	S	T	R
T	O	G	A	N	G	I	C	E	D
U	G	L	R	O	L	E	L	X	R
R	O	K	I	M	O	N	O	T	O
B	R	U	M	P	V	U	G	A	P
A	M	B	E	R	E	T	H	L	O
N	O	U	N	T	R	U	E	R	N
D	U	N	T	O	O	T	T	I	C
S	C	A	R	F	R	U	M	P	H
Y	A	T	O	F	D	N	E	T	O

THE clues listed refer to an item of clothing. Can you find the garments in our grid?

1. Japanese robe
2. Wooden shoe
3. Indian headdress
4. Neck-warmer
5. South American cloak
6. Hand-warmer
7. Brimless cap
8. Indian dress
9. Ballet skirt
10. Roman robe

B	S	I	N	P	E	S	O	L	Y
A	P	P	E	T	I	T	L	E	D
T	I	P	U	N	T	R	U	M	R
T	R	E	F	I	F	E	M	M	E
R	R	O	T	B	O	S	S	A	M
O	G	E	R	A	R	S	K	I	A
I	T	H	O	M	M	E	S	S	Y
S	O	J	U	G	E	D	H	O	G
T	R	O	G	A	R	C	O	N	E
Y	Q	R	E	P	E	L	E	G	O

TRANSLATE the following words into French and find them in our puzzle grid.

1. Man
2. House
3. Little
4. Three
5. Boy
6. Woman
7. Very
8. Red
9. Nine
10. Mother

P	O	P	L	A	Y	E	S	T	E
O	M	S	E	L	L	B	W	E	R
L	O	Q	S	A	B	R	E	A	D
I	G	U	T	R	A	O	E	R	U
C	R	E	A	M	P	L	T	O	P
E	W	E	N	U	L	L	R	F	H
U	G	N	F	D	S	E	A	S	I
R	S	S	L	O	P	R	J	T	N
I	K	K	W	I	Z	Z	A	R	D
C	Y	O	P	S	N	O	M	U	S

THE words indicated by the clues listed are all names of pop groups of the '70s and '80s. Can you find them in our grid?

1. ----- and butter
2. Traffic ---
3. ------ force
4. Pie in the ---
5. ----- of the crop
6. ----- nothings
7. --- in your eye
8. ------- of Oz
9. --- or no
10. Her Majesty the -----

```
S C O G R A N G L O
C L N L I L E I S B
H Y D E N T W L T A
U D R N E A L B O L
D E A N T R Y E N S
R E G O R C E R I A
O P U N C H I T O M
L R I C K E T O S S
L E V E R R O M E O
S Y C R E Y Z E N N
```

CAN you find the missing partner in our puzzle grid?

1. ----- and Juliet
2. Torvill and ----
3. ------ and McCartney
4. ------ and Delilah
5. Bonnie and -----
6. ------- and Sullivan
7. ----- and Judy
8. Jekyll and ----
9. Sonny and ----
10. Adam and ---

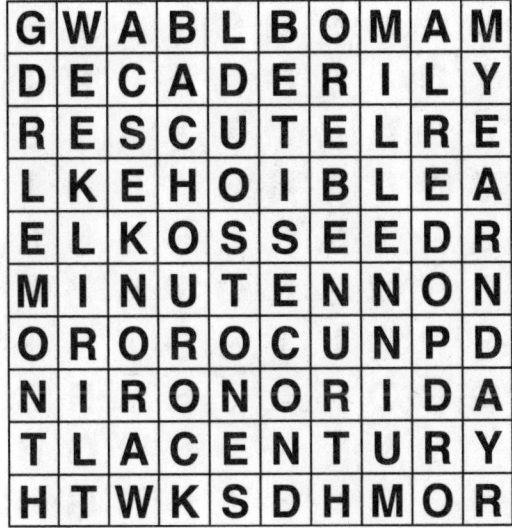

G	W	A	B	L	B	O	M	A	M
D	E	C	A	D	E	R	I	L	Y
R	E	S	C	U	T	E	L	R	E
L	K	E	H	O	I	B	L	E	A
E	L	K	O	S	S	E	E	D	R
M	I	N	U	T	E	N	N	O	N
O	R	O	R	O	C	U	N	P	D
N	I	R	O	N	O	R	I	D	A
T	L	A	C	E	N	T	U	R	Y
H	T	W	K	S	D	H	M	O	R

CAN you identify the units of time described?

1. 3,600 seconds
2. 1/120th of a decade
3. One-tenth of a century
4. 168 hours
5. 1/86,400th of a day
6. 100 decades
7. 5,200 weeks
8. 1,440 minutes
9. 365.25 days
10. 1/10,080th of a week

N	A	M	L	M	S	T	A	P	S
I	D	I	S	O	N	E	D	R	I
E	O	N	U	T	T	Y	A	I	S
C	N	D	I	H	G	A	U	N	T
E	R	I	G	E	L	S	G	C	E
R	U	M	B	R	O	T	H	E	R
E	N	G	L	I	B	O	T	S	I
S	C	O	F	A	T	H	E	R	D
I	L	V	I	Z	O	E	R	O	R
N	E	P	H	E	W	N	N	G	M

CAN you identify the family relationships?

1. Edward to John Kennedy
2. Bridget to Jane Fonda
3. Liza Minnelli to Judy Garland
4. Prince Edward to Prince William
5. Shirley MacLaine to Warren Beatty
6. Larry Hagman to Mary Martin
7. Prince William to Princess Anne
8. Marty to Kim Wilde
9. Lynn Redgrave to Natasha Richardson
10. Tippi Hedren to Melanie Griffith

E	F	C	O	R	O	B	I	R	D
W	O	L	F	A	U	S	Q	U	O
E	X	O	A	C	A	W	R	U	G
R	O	S	T	A	N	I	B	U	N
O	T	H	A	T	E	N	E	D	U
B	L	O	N	T	I	K	C	A	T
I	R	R	S	L	D	E	N	S	S
L	A	S	H	E	E	P	E	N	T
I	G	E	O	V	R	I	E	O	I
S	H	A	B	E	A	G	L	E	G

CAN you identify the animals from their related adjectives listed here? You'll find the answers in the grid written either vertically or horizontally.

1. Canine
2. Equine
3. Vulpine
4. Bovine
5. Aquiline
6. Lupine
7. Ovine
8. Avian
9. Feline
10. Porcine

I	N	L	T	O	S	P	B	E	D
C	H	A	I	R	T	D	A	R	E
U	G	M	O	A	N	L	N	A	S
P	F	P	R	S	O	F	A	O	K
B	O	D	B	O	S	W	R	G	A
O	N	O	A	S	T	O	O	L	S
A	T	N	J	F	A	T	F	Y	N
R	E	K	I	H	B	I	N	R	K
D	R	A	B	T	L	I	I	C	A
M	E	R	D	R	E	S	S	E	R

CAN you find the missing words, all making up items of furniture? Words are hidden in the grid vertically and horizontally.

1. Arm -----
2. ---- shade
3. Airing ---------
4. Water ---
5. Writing ----
6. Bar -----
7. ---- bed
8. Coffee -----
9. Welsh -------
10. Rubbish ---

E	A	S	T	R	E	S	S	P	Y
K	I	P	A	S	K	I	L	O	B
U	V	E	N	V	O	E	O	S	E
B	R	A	G	A	B	R	I	C	K
R	B	R	O	T	A	R	B	A	G
A	L	E	P	H	E	A	T	R	Y
V	I	C	T	O	R	N	K	A	M
O	C	H	E	T	O	G	O	L	F
D	R	O	M	E	O	O	I	N	K
D	R	I	P	L	F	D	L	V	I

CAN you identify the radio code words for the letters listed here? You'll find the answers in the grid written either vertically or horizontally.

1. E
2. G
3. S
4. H
5. B
6. O
7. T
8. R
9. K
10. V

B	P	C	A	S	H	P	A	A	B
R	E	U	S	I	O	L	S	T	O
E	N	T	O	P	A	F	H	G	R
A	A	O	D	E	D	B	E	R	G
G	N	B	C	S	I	E	L	W	J
A	I	A	S	L	N	C	A	Q	E
S	M	I	T	H	D	K	T	B	T
S	E	R	I	T	I	E	O	I	R
I	S	M	C	E	N	R	O	E	F
F	G	O	H	R	A	N	P	N	S

CAN you find the surnames of 10 men's champions at Wimbledon from the clues? Words are hidden in the grid vertically and horizontally.

1. Pat ----
2. Lew ----
3. Stefan ------
4. Arthur ----
5. Bjorn ----
6. Boris ------
7. John --------
8. Stan -----
9. Andre ------
10. Michael -----

T	H	R	P	S	P	L	T	N	O
W	E	L	E	A	N	O	R	E	W
I	Y	P	N	S	L	J	I	F	G
N	R	A	N	U	V	G	P	H	I
L	A	D	Y	H	L	S	P	K	C
O	Z	S	O	R	Q	T	E	I	L
V	A	W	R	I	T	E	R	T	N
E	M	A	L	T	S	I	F	R	I
E	N	N	I	G	H	T	Y	M	S
L	E	T	C	R	A	D	J	O	E

OUR word grid is hiding 10 words extracted from Beatles song titles. You'll find the answers in the grid written either vertically or horizontally.

1. --- Jude
2. ----- Lane
3. -------- Rigby
4. Day --------
5. Paperback ------
6. I ---- To Hold Your Hand
7. All You Need Is ----
8. ---- Madonna
9. A Hard Day's -----
10. --- It Be

J	A	M	O	N	M	I	C	K	L
A	R	E	T	H	A	L	L	Y	A
S	T	C	A	I	R	I	N	L	N
O	I	A	N	T	V	T	I	I	I
N	M	E	L	V	I	S	P	E	S
N	E	L	D	O	N	P	A	R	D
G	S	T	S	U	O	L	V	I	Q
H	R	O	B	E	R	T	E	A	W
F	U	N	S	U	O	I	N	L	E
O	G	E	R	Y	D	A	V	I	D

WE've given you the surnames of 10 famous vocalists. Can you find their first names? Words are hidden in the grid and written vertically and horizontally only.

1. ----- Donovan
2. ------ Franklin
3. ------ Gaye
4. ----- Presley
5. ----- John
6. --- Stewart
7. ----- Bowie
8. ------ Palmer
9. ---- Jagger
10. ------ Minogue

C	R	D	I	A	M	O	N	D	S
A	L	A	T	K	N	V	E	T	E
S	P	Y	F	R	I	J	V	L	C
I	P	L	E	K	G	Z	E	I	R
N	Y	I	D	Y	O	U	R	P	E
O	A	G	I	N	L	D	B	N	T
P	T	H	O	W	D	R	K	O	V
L	U	T	R	L	E	W	A	S	M
O	S	S	P	O	N	L	Y	I	F
F	I	J	E	B	A	N	I	L	N

CAN you find the words that make up the titles of these famous James Bond films? Words are written horizontally and vertically only.

1. ------ Royale
2. The --- Who Loved Me
3. The Living ----------
4. -------- Are Forever
5. Never Say ----- Again
6. For ----- Eyes Only
7. Man With The ------ Gun
8. On Her Majesty's
   ------ Service
9. -- No
10. You ---- Live Twice

S	W	E	E	P	E	E	C	O	P
M	R	N	C	A	T	S	O	I	I
I	N	C	O	M	A	S	O	N	G
T	I	H	S	O	N	I	P	O	O
H	D	E	F	E	N	C	E	T	C
E	G	R	I	E	E	F	R	I	A
D	R	A	P	E	R	S	O	N	D
U	O	M	A	N	G	L	W	G	D
C	O	B	B	L	E	R	N	E	I
K	M	S	O	N	T	U	A	R	E

THERE are 10 professions hidden in the grid. Can you find them from the clues we've given? Words are written horizontally and vertically only.

1. A mender of shoes
2. A metalworker
3. A leatherworker
4. A horse's attendant
5. A golfer's attentant
6. A stoneworker
7. A dealer in fabrics
8. A cleaner of chimneys
9. A maker of barrels
10. A dealer in stolen goods

L	I	M	O	U	S	E	A	B	A
O	N	U	S	N	A	I	C	L	I
E	E	L	L	U	B	D	R	A	N
N	W	E	N	T	A	B	I	R	D
G	R	A	B	B	L	I	C	R	O
N	E	R	C	L	A	R	K	E	D
E	F	S	L	O	C	T	E	N	O
A	S	P	A	R	R	O	T	T	E
B	O	O	M	G	Y	F	T	A	S
R	C	O	B	E	E	F	Y	L	I

CAN you find the animals needed to complete the similes? Words are written horizontally and vertically only.

1. As meek as a ----
2. As free as a ----
3. As stubborn as a ----
4. As chirpy as a --------
5. As busy as a ---
6. As quiet as a ------
7. As dead as a ----
8. As slippery as an ---
9. As sick as a -------
10. As happy as a ----

LUCY

50

G	A	T	P	B	R	O	J	S	O
E	L	L	R	I	C	H	A	R	D
O	D	O	F	L	S	O	M	T	W
R	O	N	A	L	D	A	E	N	I
G	T	F	E	N	H	K	S	L	G
E	S	G	S	I	A	E	T	M	H
O	B	F	H	E	R	B	E	R	T
P	A	T	I	R	R	A	S	E	M
R	J	I	M	M	Y	N	O	F	A
S	E	P	A	T	O	J	O	H	N

THERE are 10 forenames of US presidents hidden in the grid. Can you find them from the clues we've given? Words are written horizontally and vertically only.

1. ------ Washington
2. ------ Reagan
3. -------- Nixon
4. ---- Clinton
5. ----- S. Truman
6. -------- Hoover
7. ----- Carter
8. ------ D. Eisenhower
9. ----- Garfield
10. ---- F. Kennedy

G	S	T	E	W	F	K	B	E	F
W	C	N	A	B	L	O	O	A	R
O	R	A	Y	E	B	R	I	T	Y
C	A	S	S	E	R	O	L	E	D
Q	M	K	L	S	A	N	P	Y	L
T	B	M	E	S	I	M	M	E	R
L	L	A	N	O	S	F	T	O	O
S	E	R	S	T	E	A	M	P	A
L	T	E	V	W	K	R	I	N	S
C	U	R	R	Y	P	L	A	H	T

THERE are 10 cooking methods hidden in the grid. We've given you a clue, but can you find the right word?

1. Cook in a covered dish
2. Simmer in juices
3. Cook whisked eggs
4. Brown and cook in a closed pan
5. Cook in hot water
6. Boil gently
7. Cook with dry heat in an oven
8. Cook using hot water vapour
9. Cook in hot fat
10. Cook with spicy Indian sauce

S	E	V	E	N	T	Y	S	E	J
S	N	O	P	I	U	B	A	O	T
S	E	V	E	N	T	E	E	N	P
I	G	E	R	E	L	N	J	I	A
X	I	N	L	T	D	K	P	N	R
T	H	I	R	T	Y	L	A	E	F
Y	R	N	C	W	E	O	M	T	K
F	N	E	J	O	N	E	S	E	I
O	W	T	H	R	A	B	O	E	D
X	A	Y	E	S	E	V	E	N	L

THERE are 10 numbers hidden in the grid. Work out the sum and find the number? Words are written horizontally and vertically only.

1. Square root of 289
2. ? x 26 = 234
3. 3000 ÷ 50
4. 402 - 372
5. Square root of (400 -39)
6. 360 ÷ 180
7. Square root of 1
8. 2401 ÷ 343
9. 6480 ÷ 72
10. (4 x 17) + 2

F	R	O	X	S	K	A	T	E	R
A	I	I	S	T	N	D	L	O	E
N	N	T	S	E	T	P	A	K	L
D	F	R	T	W	O	L	F	I	A
V	E	E	R	N	D	I	G	K	T
I	S	L	V	O	L	M	I	O	I
W	T	N	K	I	P	P	A	L	N
R	S	T	R	I	D	E	R	E	G
P	M	O	A	M	S	D	N	U	P
A	L	I	T	E	M	F	O	L	T

YOU have two clues – an anagram and a definition. Can you find the right word?

1. West – Hotpot
2. Streak – Ice dancer
3. Fowl – Canine mammal
4. Ever – Alter direction
5. Fitness – Overruns
6. Direst – Long step
7. Emit – Thing
8. Dimple – Hobbled
9. Tar – Rodent
10. Triangle – referring

54

R	P	O	U	N	D	N	K	S	A
I	A	P	L	D	C	R	M	U	P
N	D	R	A	C	H	M	A	O	X
T	O	O	F	T	M	N	R	E	E
D	L	D	E	Y	A	H	K	P	S
E	L	I	R	A	S	F	T	M	C
L	A	R	A	P	L	I	F	Q	U
K	R	O	N	A	T	R	Y	R	D
W	G	A	S	R	O	P	E	S	O
E	F	R	A	N	C	T	N	M	E

THERE are 10 present or former currencies hidden in the grid. Can you find them using the clues of their respective countries? Words are written horizontally and vertically only.

1. Greece
2. USA
3. Sweden
4. Germany
5. Great Britain
6. Mexico
7. Japan
8. Portugal
9. France
10. Italy

I	N	D	I	A	N	T	E	R	O
N	E	E	D	L	Z	A	J	I	M
C	O	P	S	C	A	N	A	D	A
Y	R	O	M	A	M	G	M	E	L
P	I	G	A	M	B	I	A	R	T
R	N	H	U	B	I	L	I	P	A
U	G	A	N	D	A	N	C	E	R
S	L	N	D	I	F	J	A	N	P
T	U	A	R	O	R	A	H	U	L
Y	G	A	R	B	R	U	N	E	I

CAN you identify the Commonwealth countries from their capitals listed below? Words are written horizontally and vertically.

1. Kingston
2. Nicosia
3. Ottawa
4. Banjul
5. Accra
6. Delhi
7. Bandar Seri Begawan
8. Valetta
9. Kampala
10. Lusaka

B	R	E	L	B	L	A	C	K	Y
O	R	B	U	R	A	N	L	O	E
Y	E	L	L	O	W	D	O	W	W
O	W	U	S	W	S	R	A	N	H
G	R	E	E	N	T	E	R	O	I
R	A	N	G	S	R	C	I	S	T
E	R	D	I	P	U	R	P	L	E
Y	E	L	P	I	N	E	X	E	N
E	L	U	N	N	G	D	O	E	S
D	O	B	I	K	L	O	S	T	E

THE clues listed here are all shades of other colours. Can you find the colours in our grid? Words are written horizontally and vertically only.

1. Russet
2. Aubergine
3. Jade
4. Scarlet
5. Jet
6. Primrose
7. Magnolia
8. Salmon
9. Navy
10. Gunmetal

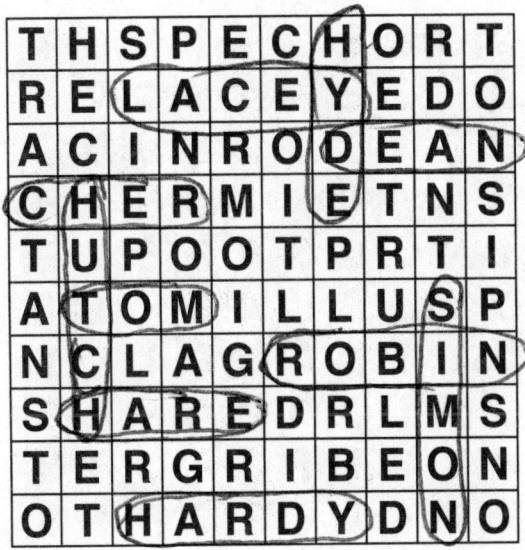

T	H	S	P	E	C	H	O	R	T
R	E	L	A	C	E	Y	E	D	O
A	C	I	N	R	O	D	E	A	N
C	H	E	R	M	I	E	T	N	S
T	U	P	O	O	T	P	R	T	I
A	T	O	M	I	L	L	U	S	P
N	C	L	A	G	R	O	B	I	N
S	H	A	R	E	D	R	L	M	S
T	E	R	G	R	I	B	E	O	N
O	T	H	A	R	D	Y	D	N	O

CAN you identify who's missing from these famous partnerships? Words are written horizontally and vertically only.

1. Simon & Garfunkel
2. Torvill & Dean
3. Jekyll & Hyde
4. Starsky & Hutch
5. Burke & Hare
6. Laurel & Hardy
7. Batman & Robin
8. Sonny & Cher
9. Tom & Jerry
10. Cagney & Lacey

N	O	B	E	G	R	I	P	S	T
D	R	I	B	K	A	N	C	V	N
O	P	G	B	A	F	L	U	D	O
D	A	N	C	R	I	O	N	A	R
I	N	D	U	C	A	R	S	V	P
D	K	O	P	L	N	E	P	I	I
O	L	S	L	A	O	P	I	P	T
G	M	T	O	M	P	A	N	E	E
H	E	A	R	T	U	R	Q	R	N
R	E	T	I	V	S	O	P	T	S

THE clues listed below describe things
better known by three or four letters.

1. Someone of eminence
2. Local time at longitude 0 degrees
3. Indication that brandy is 20-25 years old
4. Britain's airborne military
5. Nelson Mandela's organisation
6. Gravestone heading
7. Satellite music channel
8. Holland's airline
9. Request to answer an invitation
10. Licence-fee-funded TV and radio company

S	R	P	T	O	W	N	B	W	S
M	A	S	H	T	L	R	H	O	K
H	N	D	A	M	D	V	C	K	L
O	J	E	T	S	A	M	E	D	N
W	E	R	L	U	N	A	N	T	O
E	T	D	R	L	C	T	R	I	B
C	H	E	E	S	E	K	E	S	F
H	E	M	N	V	Y	D	L	O	R
I	R	H	N	P	G	B	O	N	E
H	E	A	R	T	O	G	I	G	D

CAN you find the words commonly associated with the words below? Words are written horizontally and vertically only.

1. Bangers and MASH ✓
2. This and THAT ✓
3. ––– and gown
4. Flotsam and JETSAM ✓
5. Dinner and –––
6. Chalk and CHEESE ✓
7. Here and THERE ✓
8. HEART and soul ✓
9. SONG and dance ✓
10. Skin and BONE ✓

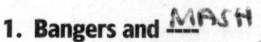

Y	E	L	L	O	W	C	P	O	G
P	L	I	T	R	N	S	I	F	R
D	A	P	L	O	R	A	N	G	E
B	L	U	E	I	E	S	K	I	E
T	N	R	P	C	D	N	B	D	N
K	E	P	A	V	O	R	H	W	H
F	B	L	A	C	K	A	N	H	O
T	U	E	N	E	A	P	L	I	R
L	E	S	K	O	Y	W	I	T	G
O	M	R	S	C	A	R	L	E	T

CAN you find the missing colours from these film titles? Words are written horizontally and vertically.

1. ---- Velvet
2. The ------ Rose of Cairo
3. ----- Narcissus
4. Clockwork ------
5. The --- Shoes
6. Pretty in ----
7. The ------- Pimpernel
8. ----- Mischief
9. Anne of ----- Gables
10. ------ Submarine

P	L	A	T	W	B	W	E	L	L
A	M	R	N	A	R	I	N	T	L
R	O	L	L	I	N	G	R	I	D
K	T	C	H	T	Y	C	P	N	H
F	H	M	I	E	S	A	L	C	O
R	E	T	R	H	V	O	D	E	R
I	R	O	O	T	K	H	A	R	S
T	W	E	A	S	R	N	I	N	E
B	I	R	D	P	R	A	M	T	O
N	A	L	T	M	U	C	K	G	P

FIND the missing word from the well-known proverbs:

1. **Necessity is the ------- of invention**
2. **A ------- stone gathers no moss**
3. **Time and tide ---- for no man**
4. **If a thing's worth doing, it's worth doing ----**
5. **The love of money is the ---- of all evil**
6. **The ---- to hell is paved with good intentions**
7. **The early ---- catches the worm**
8. **A stitch in time saves ----**
9. **Where there's ---- there's brass**
10. **You can lead a ------ to water, but you can't make it drink**

E	T	H	I	S	L	A	N	D	Y
R	V	E	R	A	N	I	A	L	O
M	O	U	N	T	A	I	N	E	F
U	L	T	O	I	L	E	R	V	O
S	C	O	D	D	R	I	V	E	R
L	A	K	E	N	D	O	N	R	E
A	N	H	S	T	I	B	U	T	S
P	O	C	E	A	N	T	S	E	T
L	I	P	R	I	E	I	E	L	A
O	W	A	T	E	R	F	A	L	L

CAN you identify the geographical features of these places? Words are written horizontally and vertically.

1. Limpopo
2. Pacific
3. Schwarzwald
4. Mediterranean
5. Honshu
6. Krakatoa
7. Niagra
8. Superior
9. Eiger
10. Kalahari

J	A	C	O	B	L	E	M	I	S
I	D	O	L	E	U	J	I	H	A
L	A	B	E	L	L	I	R	O	T
P	M	I	A	S	L	S	I	R	E
R	S	M	G	H	C	T	A	A	S
E	A	B	R	A	H	A	M	P	A
M	L	E	O	Z	O	A	B	E	U
A	E	L	A	Z	O	R	I	N	G
R	T	I	N	A	R	O	C	T	H
Y	U	G	O	R	O	N	O	A	H

CAN you identify the biblical characters from the clues listed here? All can be found in the grid, written horizontally or vertically and not backwards.

1. Cain's father
2. Cain's brother
3. Moses's brother
4. Moses's sister
5. Nebuchadnezzar's son
6. Joseph's father
7. Japheth's father
8. Jesus's mother
9. Isaac's father
10. Jacob's brother

O	N	E	V	E	J	U	N	O	R
I	D	L	E	P	U	L	O	R	G
B	I	I	N	E	P	T	U	N	E
C	A	L	U	T	I	I	S	I	N
R	N	A	S	A	T	U	R	N	S
O	A	F	A	L	E	X	O	U	T
S	S	O	M	E	R	C	U	R	Y
O	T	N	A	N	R	L	M	O	H
L	O	U	R	H	C	U	P	I	D
D	L	A	S	H	O	R	O	E	F

CAN you find the Roman counterparts of these Greek gods? Words are written horizontally and vertically.

1. Hermes, messenger of the gods
2. Aphrodite, goddess of beauty and love
3. Eros, god of love
4. Hera, queen of heaven
5. Ares, god of war
6. Poseidon, god of the sea
7. Zeus, supreme god
8. Helios, god of the sun
9. Kronos, god of agriculture
10. Artemis, goddess of the moon and hunting

C	L	R	A	F	T	A	T	U	M
A	P	I	S	L	E	N	H	Y	A
M	A	C	A	U	L	A	Y	D	S
A	S	K	L	R	I	W	H	I	O
R	K	Y	O	T	N	P	R	I	N
K	N	F	J	U	D	Y	S	F	T
E	F	W	A	Y	A	C	O	J	U
J	O	D	I	E	W	D	R	E	W
R	U	D	B	I	E	P	L	A	T
H	S	L	E	C	H	N	O	N	E

CAN you identify the first names of the child stars from the clues listed?

1. --------- Culkin (Home Alone)
2. ---- Lester (Oliver)
3. ----- Schroder (The Champ)
4. ----- O'Neal (Paper Moon)
5. ----- Gamble (Dennis)
6. ----- Blair (The Exorcist)
7. ---- Garland (Wizard of Oz)
8. ---- Foster (Bugsy Malone)
9. ---- Barrymore (ET)
10. ---- Simmons (Great Expectations)

A	V	O	L	E	N	T	A	S	P
N	L	E	O	R	T	X	E	O	L
N	V	F	A	W	M	Y	D	P	I
E	L	I	Z	A	B	E	T	H	N
A	P	N	L	T	I	S	R	I	T
S	E	G	L	O	M	B	F	A	O
M	E	R	Y	L	H	E	O	L	J
A	R	I	L	I	P	T	D	I	O
R	N	D	T	Z	D	T	G	H	A
Y	M	A	J	A	N	E	K	A	N

CAN you find the first names of these famous actresses, all of whom have won Oscars? Words are written horizontally and vertically.

1. ---- Bancroft
2. *Elizabeth* Taylor
3. ------ Bergman
4. *Meryl* Streep
5. ---- Pickford
6. ---- Minnelli
7. *Jane* Fonda
8. ------ Davis
9. ------ Loren
10. ---- Crawford

J	O	Q	U	E	E	N	E	F	T
U	P	L	T	V	L	E	W	A	W
B	O	C	A	N	B	E	R	D	E
I	W	U	G	S	K	D	E	R	E
L	E	E	R	L	G	L	I	N	Z
E	Y	L	E	X	E	E	R	I	E
E	Z	E	E	L	F	T	H	N	R
T	R	O	G	Y	M	B	K	D	S
R	I	M	P	O	F	E	T	I	G
P	E	D	I	G	R	E	E	L	R

IN the grid there are ten words with the letters "ee" in. We have given you ten clues to solve to find them.

1. Monarch
2. Sewing implement
3. To assent
4. Slippery fish
5. Buzzing insect
6. Spooky, weird
7. Line of descent of an animal
8. Look lasciviously
9. A special anniversary
10. A plucking implement

T	O	W	E	R	S	O	F	T	A
R	C	I	D	R	I	P	C	R	B
I	S	R	O	C	K	S	O	O	B
O	A	W	E	H	I	G	U	U	E
M	Y	O	L	I	B	E	R	T	Y
P	L	K	V	N	O	M	T	A	P
H	R	D	D	A	M	E	R	L	C
E	H	B	R	I	N	D	L	Y	P
T	O	I	O	V	U	R	L	T	H
R	L	G	R	A	N	D	E	S	I

CAN you find the missing word from these 10 famous tourist sights? Words are written horizontally and vertically.

1. Great Wall of _China_
2. Statue of _Liberty_
3. Hampton _Court_
4. Westminster _Abbey_
5. Notre _Dame_
6. _Big_ Ben
7. _Grand_ Canyon
8. Ayers _Rock_
9. Eiffel _Tower_
10. Arc de _Triomph_

F	A	L	L	R	M	N	I	K	F
P	A	R	D	H	O	B	O	Y	E
I	F	S	I	M	V	F	D	C	N
N	C	H	F	V	I	L	M	I	D
C	O	O	K	I	E	W	S	E	E
H	D	O	U	G	C	D	T	I	R
I	E	D	H	U	R	S	O	K	F
P	Y	W	G	A	L	G	R	O	P
O	A	P	A	R	T	M	E	N	T
F	I	N	S	T	M	U	N	K	E

CAN you find the American version of these English words? They are written horizontally and vertically only.

1. Biscuit cookie
2. Car bonnet hood
3. Potato crisp chip
4. Film movie
5. Autumn fall
6. Tramp hobo
7. Flat apartment
8. Petrol gas
9. Shop store
10. Car Bumper fender

F	R	I	M	T	O	L	R	U	P
S	U	T	H	S	H	O	A	M	A
K	Y	R	A	T	O	W	N	U	Y
R	P	O	U	R	S	M	G	I	M
I	M	D	W	E	T	R	E	K	E
B	I	D	O	A	S	I	N	L	N
E	L	E	B	M	A	R	K	E	T
A	T	N	D	I	P	L	T	O	W
T	O	S	I	C	E	P	L	A	Y
N	W	S	I	D	E	F	I	G	H

CAN you find 10 words in our grid which can all be preceded by the word 'down'? Words are written horizontally and vertically.

1. Relating to poor quality goods
2. A deposit
3. With the current
4. Central part of a city
5. Heavy burst of rain
6. Oppressed
7. In the flight path of a rocket
8. To make little of
9. Disadvantageous aspect of a situation
10. Depressed or gloomy

J	D	I	L	D	U	C	K	O	C
H	O	R	S	E	G	F	A	M	H
I	G	N	I	E	L	U	N	L	I
D	T	R	O	R	I	R	G	I	M
O	S	M	I	T	N	O	A	Y	P
L	D	E	O	T	T	E	R	E	A
P	O	V	U	T	R	I	O	W	N
H	C	C	A	T	S	W	O	I	Z
I	H	A	M	I	E	L	N	P	E
N	T	R	I	G	M	O	U	S	E

WHAT type of animal are these famous screen characters?
The answers can be found in the grid, written horizontally and vertically only.

1. Black Beauty horse
2. Donald duck
3. Bambi deer
4. Lassie dog
5. Skippy kangaroo
6. Tarka otter
7. Cheetah chimpanze
8. Jerry mouse
9. Flipper dolphin
10. Sylvester cat

B	L	U	E	S	I	L	N	O	Y
F	O	I	A	E	F	N	M	H	A
R	N	O	G	I	H	O	T	E	L
I	E	M	I	D	S	W	T	A	U
E	S	H	O	O	K	R	E	R	K
N	O	D	A	G	Y	O	L	T	R
T	M	R	I	S	A	N	O	V	L
D	E	V	I	L	C	U	M	T	O
U	L	T	O	W	I	Y	O	G	V
B	J	A	I	L	H	O	U	S	E

CAN you find the missing words from these 10 Elvis song titles? Words are written horizontally and vertically.

1. ---- Suede Shoes
2. Are You -------- Tonight?
3. All ----- up
4. ----- in Disguise
5. --------- Rock
6. ---- Me Tender
7. Hound ---
8. Heartbreak -----
9. Wooden -----
10. It's --- or Never

H	E	M	B	I	L	T	E	D	P
A	S	N	I	C	H	O	L	A	S
R	Y	K	H	A	T	L	A	V	M
D	N	W	D	R	P	D	X	I	A
A	P	E	F	O	L	I	P	D	N
R	A	L	B	L	E	A	K	O	T
G	P	O	S	U	N	G	Y	S	W
H	E	R	E	P	A	M	P	L	O
G	R	E	A	T	F	O	G	E	T
K	S	L	I	N	T	W	I	S	T

CAN you find the missing words from these 10 Charles Dickens novels? Words are all hidden in the grid.

1. -------- Nickelby
2. A Christmas -----
3. ----- Copperfield
4. The --- Curiosity Shop
5. ----- House
6. ---- Times
7. The Pickwick -------
8. ------ Expectations
9. A Tale of --- Cities
10. Oliver -----

M	A	R	G	A	R	E	T	V	A
Y	A	W	T	R	I	S	K	O	N
B	A	O	E	W	A	H	X	W	N
E	T	F	L	O	R	E	N	C	E
N	O	M	L	C	D	L	F	U	G
A	I	M	A	R	I	E	N	U	M
Z	R	I	P	L	E	N	C	I	J
I	M	E	L	D	A	V	A	P	O
R	L	I	P	R	O	T	U	W	A
F	I	M	M	A	R	I	L	Y	N

CAN you find the first names of these ten famous women? Answers are written horizontally and vertically only.

1. ---- Crawford, film star
2. ------ Marcos, key figure in Phillipino politics
3. --------- Nightingale, nurse
4. ------ Keller, blind and deaf author
5. ---- Boleyn, wife of Henry VIII
6. ------ Curie, scientist
7. ---- Fitzgerald, jazz singer
8. -------- Monroe, actress
9. -------- Thatcher, ex-PM
10. ------- Bhutto, Pakistani politician

W	O	V	U	P	R	I	G	S	T
A	D	M	I	R	A	L	F	O	B
S	F	I	M	I	E	N	D	M	E
H	A	B	U	N	A	G	C	U	L
I	G	L	E	T	T	E	R	L	E
F	H	O	W	O	A	G	O	T	P
L	I	O	U	T	P	I	S	R	H
A	M	D	E	V	E	F	S	Y	A
G	L	I	G	H	H	O	R	N	N
F	E	M	T	S	P	I	R	I	T

A PATRIOTIC puzzle. Each hidden word follows red, white or blue to make a well-known expression or name.

1. White ----, type of paint
2. Red -------, a butterfly
3. Blue -----, outline or plan
4. Red ------ Day, memorable occasion
5. White --------, something of no use
6. White ------, used to clean paintbrushes
7. Red -----, international relief agency
8. Blue -----, an aristocrat
9. Red ----, bureaucracy
10. White ----, symbol of surrender

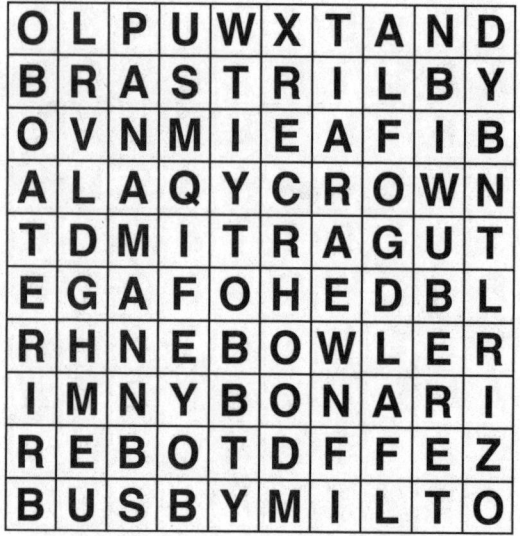

O	L	P	U	W	X	T	A	N	D
B	R	A	S	T	R	I	L	B	Y
O	V	N	M	I	E	A	F	I	B
A	L	A	Q	Y	C	R	O	W	N
T	D	M	I	T	R	A	G	U	T
E	G	A	F	O	H	E	D	B	L
R	H	N	E	B	O	W	L	E	R
I	M	N	Y	B	O	N	A	R	I
R	E	B	O	T	D	F	F	E	Z
B	U	S	B	Y	M	I	L	T	O

FIND 10 types of headgear in the grid from the clues below.
Words are written horizontally and vertically.

1. Light straw hat worn when punting
2. Soft felt hat with a dent in the crown
3. Hat named after Central American country
4. Semi-circular band of jewels
5. Royal headgear
6. Classic city gent's hat
7. An attachment to a coat
8. Classic French hat
9. Conical stiff cap, named after Moroccan town.
10. High fur hat worn by some soldiers

C	F	E	I	M	I	X	R	E	J
R	U	D	W	I	L	T	H	M	O
U	P	I	N	D	G	M	A	N	N
I	M	S	O	L	W	A	R	E	E
S	T	O	P	P	A	R	D	A	S
E	T	N	L	U	T	N	Y	Y	M
A	U	I	N	E	S	K	E	C	U
R	F	S	C	O	O	P	E	R	T
S	T	O	V	U	N	L	T	R	M
C	O	N	T	I	G	E	W	A	Y

EACH of the last names hidden in the grid belongs to a Tom, Tommy or Thomas. Can you find them all?

1. Tom ~~cruise~~, star of Top Gun
2. Thomas ------, American inventor
3. Tom --------, playwright
4. Thomas ~~Hardy~~, author
5. Tom ------, golfer
6. Tommy ------, comic magician
7. Tom -----, film star
8. Tom ---, film cowboy
9. Thomas ----, German author
10. Tom -----, singer ~~Jones~~

K	C	E	M	R	N	M	I	L	T
F	M	H	A	O	D	G	A	Y	E
M	A	S	S	E	U	R	B	E	A
O	I	P	O	G	H	O	O	F	C
S	D	R	N	S	C	O	A	C	H
L	A	V	T	D	U	M	K	I	E
H	B	A	K	E	R	L	W	A	R
N	L	L	H	C	X	F	O	R	T
S	W	E	E	P	G	P	L	M	N
K	O	T	H	I	J	U	D	G	E

HERE are 10 job descriptions. Can you find the different trades in the grid?

1. Female servant
2. Stone-worker
3. One who gives massages
4. Looks after horses
5. Trains athletes
6. Personal manservant
7. Makes bread
8. Imparts knowledge
9. Cleans chimneys
10. In legal authority

A	G	E	C	O	A	T	S	A	M
G	E	R	A	L	D	O	N	N	A
O	O	M	L	D	E	O	W	A	R
G	R	O	V	E	R	Y	H	O	T
A	G	L	I	N	S	N	E	C	I
J	E	A	N	E	R	J	O	H	N
B	R	R	T	S	H	I	R	A	G
A	B	R	A	H	A	M	P	R	A
Z	L	Y	C	L	E	M	A	R	M
Z	A	C	H	A	R	Y	D	Y	E

CAN you find the first names of these former US presidents? The answers can be found in the grid, written horizontally and vertically only.

1. ----- Truman
2. -------- Lincoln
3. ------- Coolidge
4. ---- Adams
5. ------- Cleveland
6. -------- Taylor
7. ------- Ford
8. ------- Van Buren
9. ----- Carter
10. ------- Washington

M	P	K	A	F	O	S	F	W	P
E	S	P	I	O	N	A	G	E	L
A	L	A	M	I	N	T	O	I	I
S	U	R	R	L	E	T	Y	G	T
U	N	T	K	H	E	A	N	H	M
R	P	O	L	Y	W	C	E	T	R
E	S	A	S	I	N	K	S	O	P
T	A	R	L	N	X	T	W	C	A
A	C	L	S	I	F	J	O	L	N
Q	T	E	N	O	R	P	L	N	E

THERE are 10 words in the grid which can be preceded with the word **COUNTER**. Can you find them?

1. Action to oppose
2. Spying on spies
3. Matching pair
4. A balance
5. Stub of a cheque
6. Return strike
7. Space for a screw head
8. Reduce effect
9. Bedspread
10. Highest adult male singing voice

R	I	J	O	B	F	V	I	C	E
M	T	O	V	L	I	A	M	N	O
A	D	R	A	I	N	T	D	L	T
Q	U	E	E	N	P	O	E	H	I
R	C	D	E	D	W	E	L	T	G
I	K	P	C	S	I	G	I	H	D
M	R	T	R	I	A	N	G	L	E
O	D	R	O	S	T	I	H	G	V
V	E	C	S	C	A	L	T	T	I
U	P	A	S	T	R	Y	D	O	L

FIND the word to complete these well-known phrases or titles.

1. Italian ---, film with Michael Caine
2. Venetian -----, type of window shade
3. Bombay ----, dried fish
4. African -----, film
5. Maltese -----, insignia
6. Bermuda --------, mystic area in Caribbean
7. Tasmanian ----, small ferocious animal
8. Danish -----, cake
9. Turkish ------, sweet
10. Miami ----, TV series, starring Don Johnson

S	C	L	I	C	T	E	T	X	V
M	H	F	E	M	D	I	H	Y	P
F	I	V	E	V	M	R	A	L	L
E	C	M	B	U	W	O	N	T	E
G	K	E	K	M	I	L	K	X	A
H	E	N	D	E	N	V	Y	E	S
I	N	S	P	L	E	U	O	W	E
Q	Y	F	L	O	F	S	U	N	T
C	H	E	E	S	E	L	X	I	L
L	I	J	E	N	G	F	I	S	H

TRANSLATE these French words and find their English equivalents in the grid. Words are written horizontally and vertically only.

1. Cinq *five*
2. Poulet *chicken*
3. Oui *yes*
4. Fromage *cheese*
5. Soleil *sun*
6. Lait *milk*
7. S'il vous plaît *please*
8. Poisson *fish*
9. Merci *thankyou*
10. Vin *end*

P	Z	A	M	B	L	O	Z	A	N
A	F	I	P	D	U	B	L	I	N
R	O	M	E	W	I	M	L	E	A
I	O	A	U	L	I	T	M	R	I
S	T	H	A	V	A	N	A	U	R
R	S	Y	M	I	S	K	D	C	O
W	O	L	B	E	L	T	R	K	B
V	S	U	E	U	H	J	I	L	I
R	L	O	R	I	Y	A	D	H	D
B	O	N	N	M	F	L	I	M	E

CAN you find the capital cities, past and present, of the countries listed below. They are all hidden in the grid, written horizontally and vertically only.

1. France   Paris
2. Italy   Rome
3. Republic of Ireland   Dublin
4. Spain   Madrid
5. Cuba
6. Switzerland
7. Norway
8. Germany
9. Saudi Arabia
10. Kenya

Z	L	A	M	T	U	R	N	T	S
S	O	R	T	B	I	A	A	N	I
D	O	M	O	A	L	T	T	R	Z
I	K	Y	K	T	R	S	U	I	E
N	I	G	H	T	C	H	R	L	D
V	N	S	W	I	T	R	E	U	O
E	G	W	A	M	O	L	D	T	W
C	A	B	Y	E	S	U	D	H	I
L	K	N	I	R	K	T	L	I	L
H	U	M	O	U	R	E	D	A	L

THIS should be good fun. There are 10 words in the grid which can be preceded by the word good. Can you find them from our clues?

1. Decent person
2. Act of kindness
3. Nocturnal farewell
4. General farewell
5. In a good mood
6. Fun occasion
7. Handsome
8. Of a genial disposition
9. Large enough
10. Feeling of benevolence

W	S	L	O	G	N	A	M	I	S
A	C	O	M	R	X	I	S	O	A
F	O	W	L	E	S	L	T	R	K
L	T	W	I	E	G	U	O	Y	A
I	T	M	U	N	S	H	K	L	F
J	T	L	K	E	S	E	Y	N	K
O	R	K	L	T	R	L	U	X	A
Y	S	I	A	W	O	L	F	E	U
C	K	N	S	L	I	E	M	A	Y
E	L	G	H	C	A	R	E	Y	W

THE surnames of 10 novelists are hidden in the grid. We've given you one of their books as a clue, but can you find all 10?

1. The French Lieutenant's Woman
2. Staying On
3. Brighton Rock
4. One Flew Over The Cuckoo's Nest
5. The Old Devils
6. The Trial
7. The Shining
8. Bonfire of the Vanities
9. Ulysses
10. Oscar and Lucinda

F	T	I	G	N	T	O	P	A	T
J	O	H	A	N	N	L	P	U	N
C	N	K	R	T	E	R	S	K	I
D	Y	S	Y	T	F	R	A	N	Z
O	U	E	L	Y	A	O	L	O	L
U	B	V	D	I	E	G	O	Z	P
L	R	H	Y	K	L	E	Y	I	E
T	Y	J	O	B	A	R	E	S	T
P	A	U	L	M	O	N	K	L	E
R	N	S	N	D	O	O	G	T	R

THE first names of ten former international footballers are hidden in the grid. We've given you their surname and country, can you find them?

1. Beckenbauer (Germany)
2. Miller (Cameroon)
3. Cruyff (Holland)
4. Jennings (Republic of Ireland)
5. Lineker (England)
6. Gascoigne (England)
7. Shilton (England)
8. Adams (England)
9. Robson (England)
10. Maradona (Argentina)

T	W	G	I	M	L	E	L	D	T
V	A	M	P	I	R	E	F	E	I
A	R	O	Y	U	P	V	K	M	N
R	L	P	Y	V	O	I	W	O	C
O	O	K	G	O	B	L	I	N	A
U	C	C	R	O	R	N	X	O	D
T	K	C	F	D	E	T	K	L	E
F	U	G	H	O	S	T	W	Y	V
C	N	D	U	O	J	A	M	N	I
I	M	P	H	I	T	R	O	L	L

WE have a supernatural theme here.

Find the nasties from the clues below.

1. Blood-sucking monster
2. Wicked power force
3. Sorcerer, practising black magic
4. Small, malevolent, grotesque creature
5. Religious cult involving witchcraft
6. Disembodied spirit of dead person
7. Evil spirit
8. Creature also known as Lucifer
9. Mischievous sprite
10. Scandinavian supernatural creature

O	M	V	U	L	T	E	C	D	K
I	N	H	L	O	E	E	J	Y	N
H	O	L	I	D	A	Y	J	V	O
L	S	T	F	O	U	E	I	E	C
M	E	N	T	S	K	L	T	O	K
L	R	L	P	N	X	P	L	P	A
S	P	A	R	A	D	I	S	E	R
I	M	N	E	M	X	E	W	T	E
N	O	D	P	S	H	O	D	C	A
S	L	I	H	O	N	O	U	R	M

FIND the missing word to complete these well-known phrases. All 10 are hidden in our grid, written horizontally and vertically only.

1. Busman's ----------
2. Bull's ---
3. Postman's -----
4. Fool's ---------
5. Parson's ----
6. No-man's ----
7. Shepherd's ---
8. Teacher's ---
9. Scout's ------
10. Fireman's ----

D	A	N	I	E	L	A	F	D	O
U	B	L	O	L	L	C	J	K	O
S	V	O	R	I	C	H	A	R	D
T	G	N	O	K	S	I	C	M	W
I	I	T	B	H	N	T	K	T	H
N	A	H	E	N	R	Y	G	A	B
D	P	T	R	H	U	A	S	I	E
N	A	R	T	T	I	U	J	O	N
F	U	U	C	E	X	S	Z	W	O
L	L	P	M	I	C	H	A	E	L

FIND the first names of these Oscar-winning actors. We've given you their surnames and film.

1. Day Lewis (My Left Foot)
2. Hoffman (Kramer vs Kramer)
3. Dreyfuss (The Goodbye Girl)
4. De Niro (Raging Bull)
5. Kingsley (Gandhi)
6. Nicholson (One Flew Over The Cuckoo's Nest)
7. Fonda (On Golden Pond)
8. Voight (Coming Home)
9. Newman (Colour of Money)
10. Douglas (Wall Street)

G	Y	N	M	A	W	S	T	F	I
U	M	O	R	M	A	N	W	R	C
E	T	P	Y	T	T	A	R	I	S
C	H	E	E	S	E	E	G	E	F
I	A	C	R	N	R	S	H	N	O
N	N	U	U	A	I	C	K	D	L
B	K	E	R	L	M	I	L	O	W
T	Y	F	H	O	U	S	E	U	U
C	O	I	Y	V	H	T	E	L	A
S	U	N	K	E	D	M	I	L	K

HERE are 10 well-known words from European languages. Can you find their English equivalents in the grid? Words are written horizontally and vertically only.

1. Fromage *Cheese*
2. Aqua *water*
3. Homme *man*
4. Grazia *thankyou*
5. Casa *house*
6. Amore *love*
7. Amigo *friend*
8. Lait *milk*
9. Soleil *sun*
10. Nein *no*

P	E	T	E	R	T	S	E	M	G
Z	O	B	R	A	H	U	K	I	I
S	U	Z	A	N	N	E	E	C	E
L	L	Y	U	S	T	U	O	H	R
A	R	A	O	M	O	I	R	A	I
B	I	L	L	K	C	T	S	E	W
L	K	P	U	S	A	W	F	L	I
Y	A	U	J	O	H	N	N	A	J
F	O	E	R	L	E	I	K	C	O
T	R	E	V	O	R	O	J	Y	N

CHECK the grid. Can you find the first names of 10 people who have presented news or weather programmes on television? Words are written horizontally and vertically only.

1. ----- Sissons
2. ------- Charlton
3. ------- Jonsson
4. --- Carpenter
5. ------- Buerk
6. ---- Suchet
7. ----- Stuart
8. ---- Giles
9. --- Snow
10. ------- McDonald

TEN song titles are listed below. Each title has a missing word (a verb). Can you find them in our grid?

1. House of the ----- Sun *Rising*
2. No Woman No ----- *Cry*
3. Like a ----- Stone *rolling*
4. ----- Me Rhonda *Help*
5. I Want to ----- Your Hand *Hold*
6. ----- Over Beethoven *Roll*
7. I ----- the Sheriff *Shot*
8. ----- Me In The Morning *Touch*
9. First Time Ever I ----- Your Face *Saw*
10. I Don't ----- Mondays *like*

B	V	P	O	L	T	A	I	R	E
E	M	I	I	W	I	L	L	O	W
E	L	N	S	T	E	O	F	C	U
C	H	E	S	T	N	U	T	Y	K
H	C	S	A	D	L	U	S	O	E
S	R	L	I	K	T	R	M	W	O
I	B	I	R	C	H	I	A	L	P
C	T	M	C	M	U	V	P	Y	A
D	I	E	H	U	W	H	L	G	L
Y	E	M	O	A	K	I	E	L	M

CAN you find 10 trees in our grid?
We've given you a few clues.

1. Copper -----
2. Tree used at Christmas
3. Horse --------
4. May be weeping
5. This tree produces a syrup
6. Twigs were used for corporal punishment
7. Small Asian citrus
8. Produces dates or coconuts
9. Quintessentially English tree
10. May produce nightmares

S	Y	N	R	D	I	C	E	A	T
L	A	B	O	U	R	S	D	O	T
H	N	T	M	Y	M	H	R	T	H
G	T	V	E	L	D	R	E	A	M
R	O	I	O	N	C	E	T	E	V
I	N	A	D	H	O	W	Y	L	W
A	Y	S	L	I	J	E	M	U	E
A	W	W	I	V	E	S	S	O	L
D	N	I	K	T	N	E	L	A	L
O	P	V	E	N	I	C	E	B	V

TEN titles of Shakespeare plays are listed. Each title has a missing word. Can you find them in our grid?

1. Love's ˉˉˉˉˉˉˉˉ Lost _labours_
2. ˉˉˉˉ and Cleopatra _Anto_
3. ˉˉˉˉ and Juliet _Rom_
4. A Midsummer Night's ˉˉˉˉˉ _Dream_
5. The Taming of the ˉˉˉˉˉ _Shrew_
6. All's ˉˉˉˉ That Ends Well _Well_
7. Much ˉˉˉˉ About Nothing _Ado_
8. As You ˉˉˉˉ It _Like_
9. The Merry ˉˉˉˉˉ of Windsor _Wives_
10. The Merchant of ˉˉˉˉˉ _Venice_

V	I	M	C	T	H	O	U	S	E
B	R	E	A	K	O	L	A	N	T
A	L	K	S	Z	Y	I	N	R	E
C	H	I	T	S	B	U	R	S	T
K	T	O	R	I	Z	O	U	H	C
L	I	C	R	F	I	E	L	D	D
S	A	O	U	L	W	E	O	A	L
C	L	A	S	S	V	L	O	O	K
R	K	N	T	C	O	A	B	M	R
Y	L	I	R	A	U	W	L	I	T

THERE are 10 words hidden in the grid, all of which can be preceded by the word out.

1. Occurrence of disease
2. Australian bush
3. Rejected by society
4. Adjoining building
5. Violent expression of emotion
6. Area of cricket pitch
7. Point of view
8. Fugitive
9. Surpass in quality
10. Clamour of protest

Z	O	B	R	B	A	T	E	H	K
P	O	M	C	O	R	C	V	G	R
Y	I	A	N	A	C	O	N	D	A
T	O	M	D	E	O	B	E	K	I
H	U	B	G	L	N	R	O	L	T
O	S	A	I	V	D	A	S	P	C
N	C	H	A	I	T	F	T	U	G
U	T	A	I	P	A	N	I	Y	N
E	X	P	I	E	N	T	H	K	W
T	I	G	E	R	S	N	A	K	E

Our grid is full of snakes. Can you find 10?
We've given a clue to help in each case.

1. Kaa in the Jungle Book was one
2. Very large South American snake
3. --- Constrictor
4. African green or black snake
5. Killed Cleopatra
6. Venomous snake native to Europe
7. Brown and yellow Australian snake
8. Brightly-coloured Asian snake
9. Deadly, small-headed Australian snake
10. Hooded snake

E	L	S	A	V	E	R	C	O	D
B	U	L	L	A	S	T	A	X	I
L	O	O	Z	E	C	O	P	E	L
O	S	W	A	M	O	N	E	Y	E
M	H	A	S	I	M	K	S	U	G
P	A	L	I	C	E	N	T	O	R
E	P	T	B	E	D	R	A	L	O
T	E	Z	I	A	Y	O	G	L	U
O	M	E	L	D	E	M	E	A	N
C	A	N	T	O	T	E	N	R	D

CAN you complete the titles of the Martin Scorsese films listed here?

1. The Last ---
2. --- Streets
3. The Color of ---
4. Raging ---
5. --- Midnight
6. --- Fear
7. --- Doesn't Live Here Anymore
8. The --- of Innocence
9. --- Driver
10. The King of ---

E	H	O	U	S	E	I	R	S	A
Y	A	A	G	L	I	T	K	T	G
E	N	T	E	R	P	R	I	S	E
S	D	T	I	M	C	A	H	E	N
H	S	T	L	K	O	D	Z	J	T
R	Z	S	T	Y	L	E	O	F	L
A	U	L	T	R	O	U	G	A	M
N	N	A	M	E	W	I	L	L	A
G	R	U	P	E	A	E	B	L	I
E	M	I	S	L	Y	V	O	N	I

TEN words which can all be preceded by the word **FREE** are hidden in the grid. Can you find them? We've given a clue to help.

1. Economic system
2. Person not constrained by others
3. Drawn without guide
4. Pub, not tied to a brewery
5. Unconstrained international buying/selling
6. Swimming stroke
7. Aerial sport
8. Making unforced choice
9. Happy hens
10. US word for motorway

K	A	R	V	I	D	N	I	C	D
K	E	I	T	H	D	E	A	T	U
N	S	N	L	I	Z	I	L	C	K
D	R	G	I	P	F	K	C	H	E
I	D	O	O	E	L	A	H	F	O
Z	I	T	S	T	E	W	A	R	T
Z	C	J	N	E	I	T	R	L	X
Y	J	O	C	L	M	I	L	E	S
H	O	H	I	M	T	I	I	U	S
B	E	N	N	Y	R	T	E	O	W

THE first names of 10 well-known musicians are hidden in the grid. We've given their surnames, can you find them?

1. ----- Moon (drummer)
2. ----- Starr (drummer)
3. ---- Ellington (piano)
4. -------- Parker (sax)
5. -------- Copeland (drummer)
6. ---- Coltrane (sax)
7. ----- Davis (trumpet)
8. ----- Goodman (clarinet)
9. ---- Townshend (guitarist)
10. ----- Gillespie (jazz trumpet)

100

```
Z G L E A J O B U B
H O R N P I P E T A
A G S I T G R L F L
W O V U L A V L U L
E L C L O G C Y K E
R C Y I O S S H E T
M O R R I S L D D L
W N U A O N J U M I
I G L T X W A L T Z
T A N G O N R I P A
```

CAN you find 10 dances in the grid? We've given a clue to help.

1. Performed by sailors
2. Raunchy nightclub dance
3. North country stomp
4. Classical dance
5. Provocative Middle Eastern dance
6. Rustic kicking and leaping dance
7. Folk dance with bells and sticks
8. Performed by people in single file
9. Ballroom dance in triple time
10. Performed with a rose between the teeth

CAN you find 10 sea creatures in our grid? We've given you a clue.

1. Small, spiny creature
2. Fearsome hunter
3. Sideways mover
4. Octopus-like creature
5. Favourite in tins
6. Largest living animal
7. Slippery snake-like fish
8. Aquatic mammal
9. Large game fish with long upper jaw
10. Breakfast favourite when smoked

H	I	N	P	A	N	Y	A	M	T
E	M	T	A	A	N	Z	C	T	I
R	O	F	N	D	W	E	H	R	C
A	T	D	D	T	K	M	I	I	A
O	E	R	O	S	I	J	L	S	R
J	O	L	R	I	G	U	L	L	U
A	T	L	A	S	F	Z	E	U	S
S	F	L	I	T	C	R	S	O	F
O	T	I	M	P	O	N	T	L	C
N	G	H	E	R	A	C	L	E	S

OUR theme is Greek mythology. Can you find the names of 10 gods, goddesses and lesser mortals in our grid?

1. Chief of the gods
2. He flew too near the sun
3. Boy god of love
4. Supported the heavens on his shoulders
5. Piper and herdsman
6. She opened the box of evils
7. Hero with weak spot
8. Leader of Argonauts
9. Sister consort of Zeus
10. Famed for strength

F	P	G	I	M	P	O	L	H	T
G	A	G	G	L	E	L	I	E	U
L	C	W	Y	O	N	X	D	R	N
I	K	A	B	Z	P	R	I	D	E
T	M	I	R	U	M	I	S	C	A
S	C	H	O	O	L	M	O	F	L
W	O	N	O	F	K	R	I	L	P
A	G	E	D	U	T	R	O	O	P
R	A	L	A	M	U	I	L	C	I
M	R	T	E	A	M	A	G	K	N

CAN you find the collective noun (group name) for these animals? Words in the grid are written horizontally and vertically only.

1. Geese
2. Wolves
3. Lions
4. Elephants
5. Whales
6. Bees
7. Hens
8. Monkeys
9. Oxen
10. Pigeons

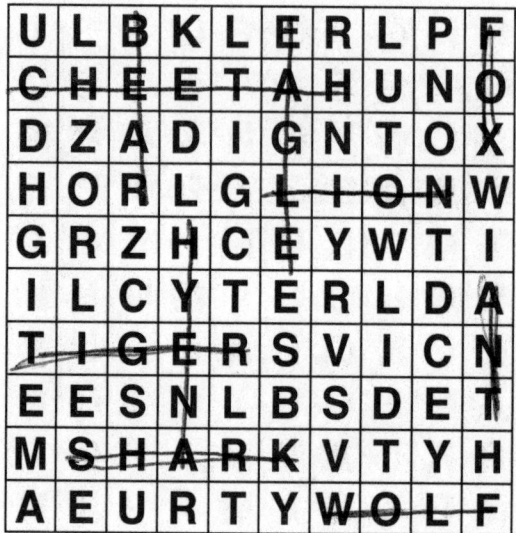

```
U L B K L E R L P F
C H E E T A H U N O
D Z A D I G N T O X
H O R L G L I O N W
G R Z H C E Y W T I
I L C Y T E R L D A
T I G E R S V I C N
E E S N L B S D E T
M S H A R K V T Y H
A E U R T Y W O L F
```

THERE are 10 predators hidden in the grid. Can you find them with the help of our clue?

1. Fastest land animal *cheetah*
2. Some of these are grizzly *bear*
3. Some of these are golden *eagle*
4. Dog-like animal *fox*
5. King of the beasts *tiger*
6. Could live in a barn *ant*
7. Largest of great cats *lion*
8. African hunting dog *hyena*
9. Predator of the seas *shark*
10. Dog-like hunter found in Europe *wolf*

F	L	I	T	C	R	O	G	F	S
K	C	H	A	R	L	I	E	T	T
H	I	A	J	L	T	R	O	S	A
F	T	R	F	I	E	J	R	C	N
A	L	O	U	S	V	L	G	Y	F
T	S	L	V	B	I	U	E	X	J
T	N	D	L	O	R	O	M	N	E
Y	E	K	D	B	U	S	T	E	R
L	M	K	I	O	S	H	Y	Y	R
W	I	L	L	B	D	A	N	N	Y

CAN you find the first names of these 10 kings of slapstick?
We've given you surnames and a film to help.

1. ------ Lewis (The Nutty Professor)
2. ---- Laurel (Way Out West)
3. ------- Keaton (The Navigator)
4. --- Hope (The Cat and the Canary)
5. ----- Kaye (Wonder Man)
6. ------- Formby (Turned Out Nice Again)
7. ---- Hay (Oh Mr Porter)
8. -------- Chaplin (The Great Dictator)
9. ------ Lloyd (The Freshman)
10. ------ Arbuckle (The Bell Boy)

G	I	C	I	S	L	P	L	U	M
C	U	R	R	Y	H	T	I	F	U
H	L	E	D	R	I	A	P	L	S
E	P	A	P	P	L	E	T	R	T
E	K	M	O	F	F	I	N	R	A
S	I	X	O	S	I	A	M	I	R
E	J	E	S	O	U	P	W	E	D
F	C	M	A	O	R	S	U	L	N
H	I	N	L	T	D	I	X	N	X
M	I	N	T	B	B	R	E	A	D

TEN types of food are hidden in the grid. Can you find them with the help of our clues? Words are written horizontally and vertically.

1. ----- favour
2. It's a ---- job
3. Cut the --------
4. ----- of my eye
5. Thick as pea ----
6. ---- of the earth
7. A ----- and butter job
8. In ---- condition
9. Chalk and -------
10. ----- of the crop

S	F	W	G	M	B	O	S	C	C
L	R	I	B	L	J	Y	E	N	L
H	E	R	O	F	W	A	R	V	I
X	E	D	D	R	P	E	U	S	M
I	Z	L	Y	U	S	D	M	E	A
N	E	N	N	O	E	F	R	L	X
D	M	C	S	G	M	H	Y	N	X
Y	A	M	K	E	I	R	I	A	I
C	H	R	I	S	T	X	S	Z	W
M	I	N	D	P	E	L	R	I	T

CAN you find 10 words which follow ANTI- to make a well-known phrase or word?

1. Rebellious character
2. Solution used in cars in winter
3. Disappointment
4. Defensive protein in the blood
5. Immunising fluid
6. Pacifist
7. Racist against jews
8. Disliking fascism
9. False messiah
10. Material preventing tyres slipping

108

X	S	L	K	P	R	I	Z	E	X
P	O	N	D	R	W	I	L	J	L
B	I	L	L	I	N	G	T	E	G
I	L	L	T	O	V	E	F	N	A
L	V	F	P	R	K	P	N	S	L
T	R	L	L	I	S	D	H	D	L
I	C	O	A	T	M	R	A	N	A
D	U	O	J	Y	P	T	T	K	N
O	W	R	E	E	L	D	W	L	T
G	I	J	N	O	T	C	H	R	P

Each word in our grid can be preceded by the word TOP. Can you find all 10?

1. Surface layer of earth
2. Most important act
3. Highest award
4. Most urgent thing
5. Highest storey
6. Leader of a group
7. Garment worn over a suit
8. Excellent
9. Type of headgear
10. Ship's mast

L	C	T	R	E	R	J	O	H	N
I	H	S	U	L	N	X	R	I	N
M	A	N	F	R	E	D	T	B	E
K	R	H	I	C	I	L	T	O	F
R	L	X	W	I	L	B	U	R	E
A	E	L	U	T	M	I	X	O	L
B	S	B	S	L	O	U	I	S	F
A	F	E	X	X	O	L	T	S	N
M	M	I	S	F	I	N	C	K	R
Y	U	R	I	Z	E	R	I	C	H

CAN you find the forenames of these 10 famous aviators?

1. -------- Von Richthofen, the Red Baron
2. ----- Alcock, first trans-Atlantic flight
3. ----- Armstrong, first man on the Moon
4. ------- Wright, one of famous brothers
5. -------- Lindbergh, solo Atlantic flight
6. ------ Bleriot, first across Channel
7. ----- Smith, first from Britain to Australia
8. ---- Johnson, woman flier
9. ----- Gagarin, astronaut
10. ------ Warsitz, first jet pilot

R	I	F	N	P	D	U	A	C	D
P	L	O	N	D	O	N	F	K	I
K	L	O	T	R	V	I	W	I	C
R	A	T	E	N	E	D	I	G	K
B	K	B	I	L	R	T	R	A	E
I	O	A	F	L	X	R	A	E	N
T	B	L	L	T	H	A	M	E	S
T	I	L	F	E	G	I	N	D	S
E	A	D	M	A	O	N	X	L	I
R	O	S	E	G	U	O	P	U	B

CAN you find 10 things associated with England?

1. One of the world's great sports
2. The capital
3. Town with white cliffs
4. Great writer
5. Large river
6. The bulk of English weather
7. The national drink
8. English drinking establishment
9. English beer
10. English flower

P	R	O	P	N	D	R	O	P	L
W	C	V	I	K	M	I	N	D	I
S	H	R	E	D	T	G	P	L	L
L	I	T	C	L	R	A	D	F	D
Z	P	R	E	W	C	O	O	R	M
B	X	O	T	P	F	I	S	N	O
I	L	C	H	A	P	T	E	R	W
T	N	E	D	R	S	K	I	C	Y
M	U	O	M	T	L	I	N	D	E
H	A	L	F	E	X	L	I	N	K

THE 10 words hidden in our grid all mean a portion or fraction. All are used in the common expressions listed.

1. Not a ------ of evidence
2. A ---- off the old block
3. A ---- in the ocean
4. A ---- of their own medicine
5. Champing at the ---
6. A ------ of my mind
7. ------- and verse
8. ---- and parcel
9. A weak ----
10. Too clever by ----

K	T	R	I	N	D	S	F	L	S
L	I	T	T	L	E	W	P	E	O
A	S	K	L	I	R	Y	A	N	N
U	A	B	F	R	E	N	C	H	E
R	M	O	W	I	K	I	E	H	A
E	S	E	W	M	R	W	T	V	N
L	R	T	L	W	L	U	P	Y	T
X	I	N	J	I	L	L	O	A	O
N	S	K	E	S	S	I	M	G	N
C	O	S	T	E	L	L	O	I	Y

CAN you find the missing partner in these famous pairings?

1. ------- and Large
2. ----- and Clive
3. Jack and ----
4. ------- and Saunders
5. Hale and ----
6. ------- and Cleopatra
7. Steptoe and ---
8. Morecambe and ----
9. Abbott and --------
10. ------- and Hardy

B	A	C	K	L	F	T	E	R	M
O	B	R	R	I	V	I	N	G	A
A	E	O	U	P	L	T	K	R	I
R	O	W	I	T	Z	I	N	C	H
D	L	N	R	V	M	I	E	O	E
M	T	H	A	M	N	G	L	V	A
I	D	E	N	A	L	E	S	U	R
E	O	A	F	S	I	X	O	X	T
M	A	R	A	T	H	O	N	L	E
L	R	I	N	J	E	A	P	K	D

YOU'LL solve this given half a chance! Each hidden word in the grid can be preceded by HALF. Use the clues listed to help.

1. Type of hotel rate
2. A position in soccer
3. British silver coin
4. Feeble-minded person
5. Short school holiday
6. Measurement
7. Wrestling hold
8. Without enthusiasm
9. Foot race
10. Position of flag

114

G	O	J	I	B	F	L	I	U	H
A	A	D	R	O	K	P	M	P	O
R	N	O	K	O	A	O	S	R	R
D	E	V	L	T	I	B	A	S	S
E	M	E	T	F	C	X	L	F	E
N	L	K	C	R	H	Y	M	I	L
L	A	C	H	E	N	L	O	S	C
Z	U	S	A	L	T	M	N	T	A
V	A	I	O	M	I	Y	R	K
Y	R	T	R	U	S	N	A	K	E

EACH of the hidden words in our grid can be preceded by **ROCK** or **ROCKING**?

1. Mixture of stones and plants
2. Australian python
3. Type of pigeon
4. Climber's footwear
5. North American fish
6. Edible fish
7. Baked sweet food
8. Children's toy
9. Type of seasoning
10. Traditional seat

L	J	I	L	T	Z	H	O	R	N
B	O	A	T	F	E	M	I	K	O
O	G	R	L	I	N	N	O	U	J
W	I	M	W	L	I	F	N	X	O
X	W	G	N	H	D	A	Z	O	H
D	I	S	T	A	N	C	E	U	N
L	N	T	R	N	A	E	X	E	S
P	D	L	I	D	S	M	C	K	E
S	E	K	L	K	T	I	M	U	N
I	D	L	R	I	F	J	U	M	P

CAN you find 10 words in the grid which can be preceded by the word **LONG**?

1. A Viking ship
2. Weapon
3. The law has this
4. Type of cattle
5. Going on and on
6. Type of telephone call
7. Type of script
8. Miserable expression
9. Athletic event
10. Warm underwear

S	P	I	D	R	I	M	A	U	W
C	A	L	A	I	S	X	L	T	I
R	R	I	N	C	E	E	F	U	N
G	I	L	B	R	I	E	W	G	E
A	S	K	I	Y	N	X	L	L	F
F	M	N	I	C	E	N	N	O	I
R	W	U	P	R	L	I	T	U	S
A	L	P	S	P	F	A	K	V	T
N	S	I	K	L	U	N	I	R	O
C	A	N	C	A	N	R	Y	E	N

CAN you find 10 things associated with France? Use the clues below to help you.

1. Channel port
2. River
3. Soft cheese
4. Alcoholic drink
5. Art gallery
6. Racy dance
7. City on the Riviera
8. Former currency unit
9. Mountain range
10. Capital city

G	K	W	I	L	F	K	O	F	K
K	A	F	K	A	G	N	K	E	I
Y	R	I	X	L	K	L	E	I	N
E	L	D	K	I	R	S	R	X	N
K	O	R	B	U	T	L	R	K	O
A	F	E	S	J	K	I	T	I	C
M	F	P	K	E	L	L	Y	R	K
R	P	K	I	L	O	U	T	K	F
K	H	A	N	I	N	D	R	L	K
T	D	L	G	M	K	E	A	T	S

THERE are 10 famous people in the grid,
all with a surname beginning with the letter **K.**

1. **Olga, Soviet gymnast**
2. **Boris, horror movie star**
3. **Franz, author**
4. **Calvin, fashion designer**
5. **Martin Luther, civil rights campaigner**
6. **Grace, movie star**
7. **Neil, former UK Labour leader**
8. **Deborah, actress**
9. **John, poet**
10. **Imran, former Pakistan cricket captain**

T	Y	I	C	R	U	L	M	A	Y
R	A	C	R	F	O	D	P	L	I
A	M	N	E	S	T	Y	V	I	L
R	B	Z	A	E	X	N	W	O	A
M	I	C	M	N	J	A	M	M	Y
Y	Q	U	Y	L	D	M	L	D	M
F	S	T	D	N	I	O	R	I	A
M	A	R	R	Y	K	G	S	K	N
R	Q	O	N	M	J	I	H	L	H
P	Y	J	A	M	A	S	L	C	G

TEN words in the grid have one thing in common – they all contain the letters M, A and Y. Can you find them?

1. Military force
2. General pardon
3. Tropical vegetable
4. Electricity generator
5. On top of the milk
6. Slang for lucky
7. One without technical knowledge
8. Wed
9. Month of the year
10. Worn in bed

J	I	C	K	F	L	E	X	L	G
S	O	R	T	S	T	U	L	T	E
I	L	I	P	F	O	S	D	W	N
G	W	S	P	I	T	E	T	I	E
N	X	O	C	N	R	R	N	C	R
E	I	L	H	E	I	V	E	L	A
D	J	V	Z	F	S	E	L	K	T
N	Y	E	O	L	P	D	S	O	I
S	E	M	H	I	E	R	I	M	O
L	A	T	E	K	C	T	U	R	N

EACH of the hidden words in our grid can be preceded by RE. Can you find all 10?

1. Accepting your fate
2. Holiday town
3. Purify
4. Instinctive reaction
5. Being born again
6. Cool in manner
7. Pause
8. Decide firmly
9. Come back
10. Tell or narrate

X	F	O	R	M	A	N	V	O	S
R	O	M	E	P	R	A	W	U	T
E	S	P	D	E	M	M	E	S	O
S	S	L	F	I	N	R	L	L	N
P	E	K	O	M	L	T	L	Y	E
C	L	N	R	N	A	U	E	N	U
F	O	R	D	X	N	H	S	D	L
T	J	E	U	L	G	W	R	O	E
W	O	N	M	R	M	T	I	L	A
I	V	E	K	H	U	S	T	O	N

CAN you find the surnames of 10 famous film directors?

1. Milos ------ (One Flew Over the Cuckoo's Nest)
2. Oliver ----- (Platoon)
3. Jonathan ----- (Silence of the Lambs)
4. Orson ------- (Citizen Kane)
5. Robert -------- (Ordinary People)
6. John ---- (My Darling Clementine)
7. David ---- (Bridge On the River Kwai)
8. John ------ (The African Queen)
9. Fritz ---- (Metropolis)
10. Bob ----- (Cabaret)

Wordpuzzler
Solutions

Solution 1

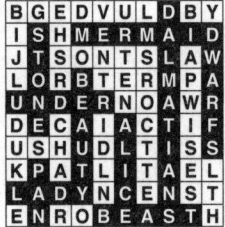

1 Gigi 2. Camelot 3. My Fair Lady
4. Oliver 5. Hair 6. Cats 7. Oklahoma!
8. Show Boat 9. Chess 10. Evita

Solution 2

1. Tolstoy 2. Tolkien 3. Defoe 4. Swift
5. Hugo 6. Dumas 7. Austen 8. Orwell
9. Dickens 10. Verne

Solution 3

1. Lady 2. Under 3. Pan 4. Dwarfs
5. Mermaid 6. Beauty 7. Stone
8. Dalmatians 9. Beast 10. Alice

Solution 4

1. Twenty 2. Eleven 3. Six 4. Ten
5. Fifteen 6. Seven 7. Nine 8. Three
9. Eight 10. Five

Solution 5

1. Liver 2. Joint 3. Stomach 4. Nerve
5. Nose 6. Skin 7. Ear 8. Kidney 9. Gums
10. Eye

Solution 6

1. Newman 2. Brando 3. Kelly 4. Dean
5. Cooper 6. Bogart 7. Grant 8. Gable
9. Wayne 10. Gere

Solution 7

```
A G O N D O L A S T
T T V E I B V C O G
T R A M P R A C E R
G I N A P P L A N E
A C H E T R U B L Y
S K A C A M E L I H
U S T E X O N E R O
C H R O I M P C J U
R A F T E T R A I N
E W G A R T Y R O D
```

1. Taxi 2. Greyhound 3. Tram 4. Camel
5. Raft 6. Plane 7. Rickshaw 8. Train
9. Gondola 10. Cable car

Solution 8

```
R I N C A I R O N W
O S L O U T H R L I
S O P P L A M M A N
T F R E D L O N G T
E I I N B O U T O F
B A T H E N S I S E
S Q U A L M E X H E
I M T G L O O K E S
N E A E T R U J L T
B E R N I E L I M A
```

1. Bern 2. Lima 3. Athens 4. Seoul
5. Copenhagen 6. Lagos 7. Sofia 8. Oslo
9. Amman 10. Cairo

Solution 9

```
V A M T T H E N I B
C B R O W A N A S Z
U B L A D R O U T E
K O P S I D E C O P
E T E S P Y T H O N
S T C K R E I U G H
M O R E C A M B E T
A C A D O R G L S O
R A Z O N F H O S P
X R Y G A L L E N T
```

1. Hardy 2. Kops 3. Morecambe
4. Stooges 5. Crazy 6. Rowan 7. Python
8. Allen 9. Marx 10. Abbott

Solution 10

```
O U N C E R S I V A
N N E E L O K N O T
C P X N A G R G L H
A E B T W A I R T E
M R U I N L P E A L
P N S M I L E A P I
E E U E L O P T S T
R E S T O N E A T R
E T N R E G L U T E
D U D E C I B E L T
```

1. Volt 2. Mile 3. Litre 4. Ounce
5. Ampere 6. Centimetre 7. Knot
8. Gallon 9. Decibel 10. Stone

Solution 11

```
T S U G A R C A N E
M I N O N B I W R G
T R E S I N G L O G
R U D L S T H A J R
I P A W E B E R U I
P E P P E R M I N T
L S P U D I C X I H
U B L I N G R A P E
M E E D O G A V E N
P U D U C H E R R Y
```

1. Apple 2. Cherry 3. Resin 4. Aniseed
5. Juniper 6. Egg 7. Peppermint 8. Plum
9. Sugar Cane 10. Grape

Solution 12

```
E D U S B R O W N S
N I J P R E A Y K O
D G R U N D R A B L
M G O R B I N B U F
T R I P P A B L U E
Y E L L O W N A R M
H Y P E S H O C I N
T E E S P I N K L I
O G R M O T H I L L
L O G R E E N T H E
```

1. Green 2. Grey 3. Yellow 4. Blue 5. Red
6. Purple 7. Brown 8. Pink 9. Black
10. White

Solution 13

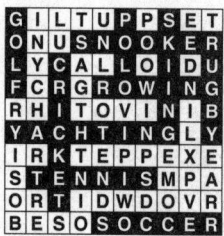

```
G I L T U P P S E T
O N U S N O O K E R
L Y C A L L O I D U
F C R G R O W I N G
R H I T O V I N I B
Y A C H T I N G L Y
I R K T E P P E X E
S T E N N I S M P A
O R T I D W D O V R
B E S O S O C C E R
```

1. Skiing 2. Rowing 3. Cricket 4. Polo
5. Golf 6. Rugby 7. Yachting 8. Soccer
9. Snooker 10. Tennis

Solution 14

```
B Z R U F L E D F S
J E A N O H E N R Y
H A R I L A J O A L
E R I K R T L O N E
L U G L A T R A Z D
U W O L F G A N G W
D H R P E J L S T A
W O P P L R P O S R
I V E R I C H A R D
G I N O X M A S A X
```

1. Felix 2. Jean 3. Henry 4. Richard
5. Igor 6. Franz 7. Wolfgang 8. Edward
9. Ralph 10. Ludwig

Solution 15

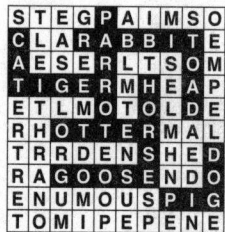

```
S T E G P A I M S O
C L A R A B B I T E
A E S E R L T S O M
T I G E R M H E A P
E T L M O T O L D E
R H O T T E R M A L
T R R D E N S H E D
R A G O O S E N D O
E N U M O U S P I G
T O M I P E P E N E
```

1. Otter 2. Rabbit 3. Dog 4. Horse 5. Pig
6. Toad 7. Parrot 8. Tiger 9. Goose
10. Cat

Solution 16

```
P A R I S S R E T M
S T O W I T O K Y O
H E V A B I D U P N
E R O D E Y E L A T
L I C H R O M E L R
S E O U L D O R A E
I N M A I R S C A A
N O M U N I C H Y L
K I T R G F O E G A
I G I A N T W E R P
```

1. Rome 2. Moscow 3. Helsinki
4. Montreal 5. Berlin 6. Antwerp 7. Seoul
8. Tokyo 9. Paris 10. Munich

Solution 17

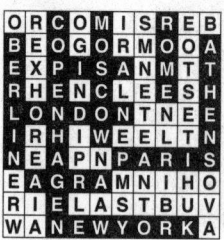

```
O R C O M I S R E B
B E O G O R M O O A
E X P I S A N M T T
R H E N C L E E S H
L O N D O N T N E E
I R H I W E E L T N
N E A P N P A R I S
E A G R A M N I H O
R I E L A S T B U V
W A N E W Y O R K A
```

1. Paris 2. Copenhagen 3. Athens
4. Berlin 5. London 6. Pisa 7. Agra
8. New York 9. Rome 10. Moscow

Solution 18

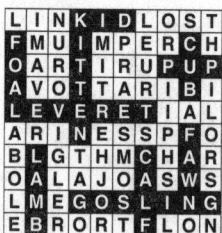

```
L I N K I D L O S T
F M U I M P E R C H
O A R T I R U P U P
A V O T T A R I B I
L E V E R E T I A L
A R I N E S S P F O
B L G T H M C H A R
O A L A J O A S W S
L M E G O S L I N G
E B R O R T F L O N
```

1. Calf 2. Kitten 3. Lamb 4. Fawn 5. Kid
6. Gosling 7. Leveret 8. Pup 9. Foal
10. Cub

Solution 19

```
D R U M S A V E S T
O E G I T S   T A R
H A R P O L O A X E
S P L A C E L L O W
D U G N K W I S P H
F L U T E R N C H O
B L I I N E T H O M
L E T R A P I A N O
S C A O L U Z R E T
I T R U M P E T E R
```

1. Flute 2. Drums 3. Saxophone
4. Harp 5. Piano 6. Violin 7. Guitar
8. Cello 9. Trumpet 10. Sitar

Solution 20

```
T A S T I C L S I T
A S K U L L Y C R I
S U R B I A P A L B
C R I B L V A P R I
V E B I F I B U L A
L S U S H C E L I B
M P A T E L L A X T
E I N E J E G R J I
R N I R U W R E A D
F E M U R D E N W O
```

1. Scapula 2. Spine 3. Rib 4. Tibia
5. Clavicle 6. Jaw 7. Patella 8. Femur
9. Skull 10. Fibula

Solution 21

```
R E A R H O N E S A
H R B T O R E D A C
I G O R L N R O Y L
N A N O L I F F E Y
E N C D I L M N V D
X T H A M E S T I E
F I R N U N G L E C
N B O U R S E I N E
G E L B E N G N T N
P R E E S T R I O K
```

1. Danube 2. Seine 3. Clyde 4. Rhine
5. Thames 6. Elbe 7. Liffey 8. Tiber
9. Rhone 10. Nile

Solution 22

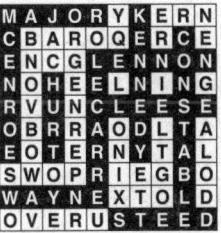

```
M A J O R Y K E R N
C B A R O Q E R C E
E N C G L E N N O N
N O H E E L N I N G
R V U N C L E E S E
O B R R A O D L T A
E O T E R N Y T A L
S W O P R I E G B O
W A Y N E X T O L D
O V E R U S T E E D
```

1. Wayne 2. Major 3. McEnroe 4. Cleese
5. Constable 6. Kennedy 7. Steed
8. Le Carré 9. Hurt 10. Lennon

Solution 23

```
I O A W Y M O I N G
L O U I S I A N A E
L I T L E C L E D F
I T A K A H O V I L
N E H W H I D A H O
O X E M A G E D A R
I S O A H A W A I I
S A H T O N A M N D
O V I Y M O N A T A
Y C O L O R A D O T
```

1. Utah 2. Florida 3. Colorado 4. Michigan
5. Idaho 6. Hawaii 7. Illinois 8. Ohio
9. Louisiana 10. Nevada

Solution 24

```
E S H W A M A B E R
S P I E L B E R G A
C A T L L E B O G D
O S C S E R F O R D
R I H L N R G K I E
S R C E R C A S O R
E N O S K A R A L B
S A C O P P O L A I
E N K I R R W I N N
S L E L E A N A G L
```

1. Coppola 2. Hitchcock 3. Lang 4. Ford
5. Scorsese 6. Lean 7. Spielberg
8. Brooks 9. Allen 10. Capra

Solution 25

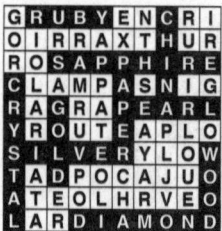

G	R	U	B	Y	E	N	C	R	I
O	I	R	R	A	X	T	H	U	R
R	O	S	A	P	P	H	I	R	E
C	L	A	M	P	A	S	N	I	G
R	A	G	R	A	P	E	A	R	L
Y	R	O	U	T	E	A	P	L	O
S	I	L	V	E	R	Y	L	O	W
T	A	D	P	O	C	A	J	U	O
A	T	E	O	L	H	R	V	E	O
L	A	R	D	I	A	M	O	N	D

1. Diamond 2. Ruby 3. Crystal 4. Gold
5. Pearl 6. Wood 7. China 8. Sapphire
9. Paper 10. Silver

Solution 26

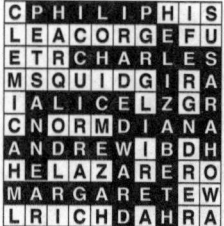

C	P	H	I	L	I	P	H	I	S
L	E	A	C	O	R	G	E	F	U
E	T	R	C	H	A	R	L	E	S
M	S	Q	U	I	D	G	I	R	A
I	A	L	I	C	E	L	Z	G	R
C	N	O	R	M	D	I	A	N	A
A	N	D	R	E	W	I	B	D	H
H	E	L	A	Z	A	R	E	R	O
M	A	R	G	A	R	E	T	E	W
L	R	I	C	H	D	A	H	R	A

1. Andrew 2. Sarah 3. Charles 4. Diana
5. Elizabeth 6. Philip 7. Edward 8. Alice
9. Anne 10. Margaret

Solution 27

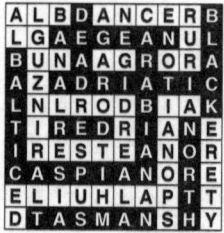

A	L	B	D	A	N	C	E	R	B
L	G	A	E	G	E	A	N	U	L
B	U	N	A	A	G	R	O	R	A
A	Z	A	D	R	I	A	T	I	C
L	N	L	R	O	D	B	I	A	K
T	I	R	E	D	R	I	A	N	E
I	R	E	S	T	E	A	N	O	R
C	A	S	P	I	A	N	O	R	E
E	L	I	U	H	L	A	P	T	T
D	T	A	S	M	A	N	S	H	Y

1. Baltic 2. Black 3. North 4. Adriatic
5. Tasman 6. Dead 7. Caspian 8. Aegean
9. Red 10. Arabian

Solution 28

S	U	C	R	E	E	F	P	N	U
T	R	I	A	N	G	L	E	I	S
O	D	R	Y	C	R	U	N	J	P
P	O	C	D	A	S	G	T	H	H
Y	E	L	O	S	Q	U	A	R	E
R	W	E	H	P	R	N	G	E	R
A	N	D	M	I	S	C	O	N	E
M	R	U	K	R	I	L	N	A	T
I	M	P	L	A	N	E	T	R	I
D	I	P	U	L	S	C	U	B	E

1. Square 2. Sphere 3. Triangle
4. Pyramid 5. Cube 6. Pentagon 7. Circle
8. Cone 9. Plane 10. Spiral

Solution 29

R	D	I	E	T	R	I	C	H	A
O	R	I	V	A	N	A	M	E	L
B	R	D	A	Y	A	G	N	T	E
A	U	R	A	L	W	A	S	H	N
C	L	E	M	O	N	R	O	E	X
A	A	B	O	R	I	L	U	P	H
L	S	I	R	D	G	A	R	B	O
L	E	I	G	H	T	N	O	U	R
E	L	G	A	O	E	D	P	R	U
O	F	O	N	D	A	R	I	N	G

1. Hepburn 2. Bacall 3. Fonda 4. Taylor
5. Leigh 6. Dietrich 7. Garland 8. Monroe
9. Day 10. Garbo

Solution 30

B	R	O	A	D	W	A	Y	R	S
E	A	M	G	R	O	V	L	A	T
W	V	A	D	I	A	R	O	D	R
A	E	R	U	V	D	I	T	C	E
L	N	C	R	E	S	C	E	N	T
K	U	L	H	I	L	W	R	V	E
T	B	O	U	L	V	A	R	D	M
R	I	S	E	O	P	L	A	C	E
E	V	E	N	U	R	Y	C	I	W
T	R	U	G	A	R	D	E	N	S

1. Place 2. Rise 3. Mews 4. Drive
5. Gardens 6. Terrace 7. Broadway
8. Close 9. Walk 10. Crescent

Solution 31

```
C O S I D D R A G A
R I P R O G I L I B
E B U L U R B R I L
L O B A B Y L O R A
A J L I L E E J O C
C H I N E S E A W K
I I C G A H S M H E
D U K R R E D A O D
O W L I F E E I M R
N T E P S T I M E Y
```

1. Public 2. Home 3. Life 4. Double
5. Acid 6. Black 7. Chinese 8. Sheet
9. Time 10. Baby

Solution 32

```
D P O R I P E N A L
R E V A L C N A M A
O B I T C H I N A M
V E X I W I E N U P
U J E W E R P Y R A
H E N D R O E G A D
A L T A S K L O C O
I L E N C O M A R E
R Y R G O F E T O S
W O S O W E R O W N
```

1. Ewe 2. Mare 3. Hen 4. Cow
5. Nanny goat 6. Bitch 7. Vixen 8. Sow
9. Doe 10. Pen

Solution 33

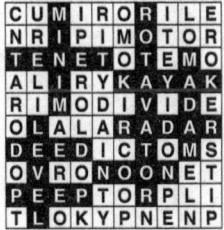

```
C U M I R O R I L E
N R I P I M O T O R
T E N E T O T E M O
A L I R Y K A Y A K
R I M O D I V I D E
O L A L A R A D A R
D E E D I C T O M S
O V R O N O O N E T
P E E P T O R P L I
T L O K Y P N E N P
```

1. Noon 2. Madam 3. Tenet 4. Deed
5. Kayak 6. Level 7. Minim 8. Rotavator
9. Peep 10. Radar

Solution 34

```
T D O L L Y M U R L
H A R D Y C A S N E
R R B U S U P N U B
I K A C L O S E T I
B S C K I R E T L G
O R H I T I P H O H
S H O R T S I I B T
M I T R L O N G A T
O F I N E L O H B E
A F A R I S I S S K
```

1. Close 2. High 3. Far 4. Short 5. Little
6. Dark 7. Long 8. Hot 9. Hard 10. Big

Solution 35

```
S L I S P I N S T R
T O G A N G I C E D
U G L R O L E L X R
R O K I M O N O T O
B R U M P V U G A P
A M B E R E T H L O
N O U N T R U E R N
D U N T O O T T I C
S C A R F R U M P H
Y A T O F D N E T O
```

1. Kimono 2. Clog 3. Turban 4. Scarf
5. Poncho 6. Glove 7. Beret 8. Sari
9. Tutu 10. Toga

Solution 36

```
B S I N P E S O L Y
A P P E T I T L E D
T I P U T R U M R
T R E F I F E M M E
R R O T B O S S A M
O G E R A R S K I A
I T H O M M E S S Y
S O J U G E D H O G
T R O G A R C O N E
Y Q R E P E L E G O
```

1. Homme 2. Maison 3. Petit 4. Trois
5. Garçon 6. Femme 7. Très 8. Rouge
9. Neuf 10. Mère

Solution 37

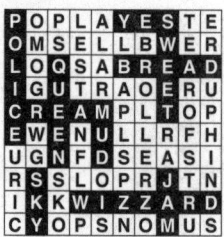

1. Bread 2. Jam 3. Police 4. Sky
5. Cream 6. Sweet 7. Mud 8. Wizzard
9. Yes 10. Queen

Solution 38

1. Romeo 2. Dean 3. Lennon 4. Samson
5. Clyde 6. Gilbert 7. Punch 8. Hyde
9. Cher 10. Eve

Solution 39

1. Hour 2. Month 3. Decade 4. Week
5. Second 6. Millenium 7. Century 8. Day
9. Year 10. Minute

Solution 40

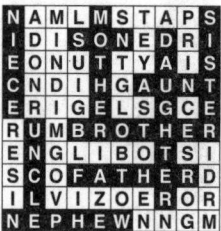

1. Brother 2. Niece 3. Daughter 4. Uncle
5. Sister 6. Son 7. Nephew 8. Father
9. Aunt 10. Mother

Solution 41

1. Dog 2. Horse 3. Fox 4. Cattle 5. Eagle
6. Wolf 7. Sheep 8. Bird 9. Cat 10. Pig

Solution 42

1. Chair 2. Lamp 3. Cupboard 4. Bed
5. Desk 6. Stool 7. Sofa 8. Table
9. Dresser 10. Bin

Solution 43

1. Echo 2. Golf 3. Sierra 4. Hotel 5. Bravo
6. Oscar 7. Tango 8. Romeo 9. Kilo
10. Victor

Solution 44

1. Cash 2. Hoad 3. Edberg 4. Ashe
5. Borg 6. Becker 7. McEnroe 8. Smith
9. Agassi 10. Stich

Solution 45

1. Hey 2. Penny 3. Eleanor 4. Tripper
5. Writer 6. Want 7. Love 8. Lady
9. Night 10. Let

Solution 46

1. Jason 2. Aretha 3. Marvin 4. Elvis
5. Elton 6. Rod 7. David 8. Robert
9. Mick 10. Kylie

Solution 47

CRDIAMONDS
ALATKNVETE
SPYFRIJVLC
IPLEKGZEIR
NYIDYOURPE
OAGINLDBNT
PTHOWDRKOV
LUTRLEWASM
OSSPONLYIF
FIJEBANILN

1. Casino 2. Spy 3. Daylights 4. Diamonds
5. Never 6. Your 7. Golden 8. Secret
9. Dr 10. Only

Solution 48

SWEEPEECOP
MRNCATSOII
INCOMASONG
TIHSONIPOO
HDEFENCETC
EGRIEEFRIA
DRAPERSOND
UOMANGLWGD
COBBLERNEI
KMSONTUARE

1. Cobbler 2. Smith 3. Tanner 4. Groom
5. Caddie 6. Mason 7. Draper 8. Sweep
9. Cooper 10. Fence

Solution 49

1. Lamb 2. Bird 3. Mule 4. Cricket
5. Bee 6. Mouse 7. Dodo 8. Eel 9. Parrot
10. Lark

Solution 50

1. George 2. Ronald 3. Richard 4. Bill
5. Harry 6. Herbert 7. Jimmy 8. Dwight
9. James 10. John

Solution 51

1. Casserole 2. Stew 3. Scramble
4. Braise 5. Boil 6. Simmer 7. Roast
8. Steam 9. Fry 10. Curry

Solution 52

1. Seventeen 2. Nine 3. Sixty 4. Thirty
5. Nineteen 6. Two 7. One 8. Seven
9. Ninety 10. Seventy

Solution 53

1. Stew 2. Skater 3. Wolf 4. Veer
5. Infests 6. Stride 7. Item 8. Limped
9. Rat 10. Relating

Solution 54

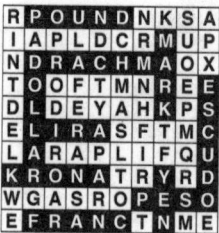

1. Drachma 2. Dollar 3. Krona 4. Mark
5. Pound 6. Peso 7. Yen 8. Escudo
9. Franc 10. Lira

Solution 55

1. Jamaica 2. Cyprus 3. Canada
4. Gambia 5. Ghana 6. India 7. Brunei
8. Malta 9. Uganda 10. Zambia

Solution 56

1. Brown 2. Purple 3. Green 4. Red
5. Black 6. Yellow 7. White 8. Pink
9. Blue 10. Grey

Solution 57

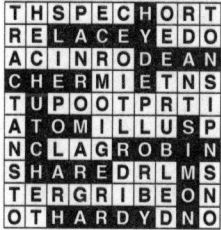

1. Simon 2. Dean 3. Hyde 4. Hutch
5. Hare 6. Hardy 7. Robin 8. Cher 9. Tom
10. Lacey

Solution 58

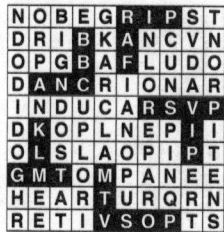

1. VIP 2. GMT 3. VSOP 4. RAF 5. ANC
6. RIP 7. MTV 8. KLM 9. RSVP 10. BBC

Solution 59

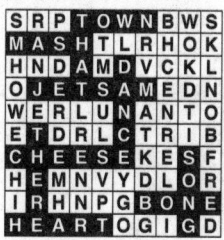

1. Mash 2. That 3. Town 4. Jetsam
5. Dance 6. Cheese 7. There 8. Heart
9. Song 10. Bone

Solution 60

1. Blue 2. Purple 3. Black 4. Orange
5. Red 6. Pink 7. Scarlet 8. White
9. Green 10. Yellow

Solution 61

1. Mother 2. Rolling 3. Wait 4. Well
5. Root 6. Road 7. Bird 8. Nine 9. Muck
10. Horse

Solution 62

1. River 2. Ocean 3. Forest 4. Sea
5. Island 6. Volcano 7. Waterfall 8. Lake
9. Mountain 10. Desert

Solution 63

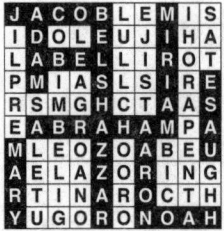

1. Adam 2. Abel 3. Aaron 4. Miriam
5. Belshazzar 6. Jacob 7. Noah 8. Mary
9. Abraham 10. Esau

Solution 64

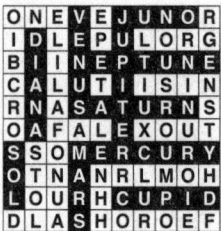

1. Mercury 2. Venus 3. Cupid 4. Juno
5. Mars 6. Neptune 7. Jupiter 8. Sol
9. Saturn 10. Diana

Solution 65

1. Macaulay 2. Mark 3. Ricky 4. Tatum
5. Mason 6. Linda 7. Judy 8. Jodie
9. Drew 10. Jean

Solution 66

1. Anne 2. Elizabeth 3. Ingrid 4. Meryl
5. Mary 6. Liza 7. Jane 8. Bette 9. Sophia
10. Joan

Solution 67

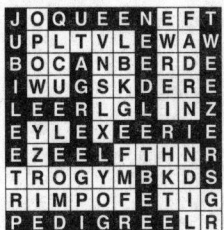

1. Queen 2. Needle 3. Agree 4. Eel
5. Bee 6. Eerie 7. Pedigree 8. Leer
9. Jubilee 10. Tweezers

Solution 68

1. China 2. Liberty 3. Court 4. Abbey
5. Dame 6. Big 7. Grand 8. Rock
9. Tower 10. Triomphe

Solution 69

1. Cookie 2. Hood 3. Chip 4. Movie
5. Fall 6. Hobo 7. Apartment 8. Gas
9. Store 10. Fender

Solution 70

1. Market 2. Payment 3. Stream 4. Town
5. Pour 6. Trodden 7. Range 8. Play
9. Side 10. Beat

Solution 71

1. Horse 2. Duck 3. Deer 4. Dog
5. Kangaroo 6. Otter 7. Chimpanzee
8. Mouse 9. Dolphin 10. Cat

Solution 72

1. Blue 2. Lonesome 3. Shook 4. Devil
5. Jailhouse 6. Love 7. Dog 8. Hotel
9. Heart 10. Now

Solution 73

H	E	M	B	I	L	T	E	D	P
A	S	N	I	C	H	O	L	A	S
R	Y	K	H	A	T	L	A	V	M
D	N	W	D	R	P	D	X	I	A
A	P	E	F	O	L	I	P	D	N
R	A	L	B	L	E	A	K	O	T
G	P	O	S	U	N	G	Y	S	W
H	E	R	E	P	A	M	P	L	O
G	R	E	A	T	F	O	G	E	T
K	S	L	I	N	T	W	I	S	T

1. Nicholas 2. Carol 3. David 4. Old
5. Bleak 6. Hard 7. Papers 8. Great
9. Two 10. Twist

Solution 74

M	A	R	G	A	R	E	T	V	A
Y	A	W	T	R	I	S	K	O	N
B	A	O	E	W	A	H	X	W	N
E	T	F	L	O	R	E	N	C	E
N	O	M	L	C	D	L	F	U	G
A	I	M	A	R	I	E	N	U	M
Z	R	I	P	L	E	N	C	I	J
I	M	E	L	D	A	V	A	P	O
R	L	I	P	R	O	T	U	W	A
F	I	M	M	A	R	I	L	Y	N

1. Joan 2. Imelda 3. Florence 4. Helen
5. Anne 6. Marie 7. Ella 8. Marilyn
9. Margaret 10. Benazir

Solution 75

W	O	V	U	P	R	I	G	S	T
A	D	M	I	R	A	L	F	O	B
S	F	I	M	I	E	N	D	M	E
H	A	B	U	N	A	G	C	U	L
I	G	L	E	T	T	E	R	L	E
F	H	O	W	O	A	G	O	T	P
L	I	O	U	T	P	I	S	R	H
A	M	D	E	V	E	F	S	Y	A
G	L	I	G	H	H	O	R	N	N
F	E	M	T	S	P	I	R	I	T

1. Wash 2. Admiral 3. Print 4. Letter
5. Elephant 6. Spirit 7. Cross 8. Blood
9. Tape 10. Flag

Solution 76

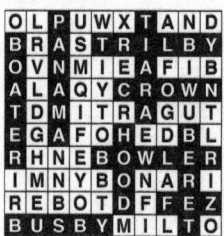

O	L	P	U	W	X	T	A	N	D
B	R	A	S	T	R	I	L	B	Y
O	V	N	M	I	E	A	F	I	B
A	L	A	Q	Y	C	R	O	W	N
T	D	M	I	T	R	A	G	U	T
E	G	A	F	O	H	E	D	B	L
R	H	N	E	B	O	W	L	E	R
I	M	N	Y	B	O	N	A	R	I
R	E	B	O	T	D	F	F	E	Z
B	U	S	B	Y	M	I	L	T	O

1. Boater 2. Trilby 3. Panama 4. Tiara
5. Crown 6. Bowler 7. Hood 8. Beret
9. Fez 10. Busby

Solution 77

C	F	E	I	M	I	X	R	E	J
R	U	D	W	I	L	T	H	M	O
U	P	I	N	D	G	M	A	N	N
I	M	S	O	L	W	A	R	E	E
S	T	O	P	P	A	R	D	A	S
E	T	N	L	U	T	N	Y	Y	M
A	U	I	N	E	S	K	E	C	U
R	F	S	C	O	O	P	E	R	T
S	T	O	V	U	N	L	T	R	M
C	O	N	T	I	G	E	W	A	Y

1. Cruise 2. Edison 3. Stoppard 4. Hardy
5. Watson 6. Cooper 7. Conti 8. Mix
9. Mann 10. Jones

Solution 78

K	C	E	M	R	N	M	I	L	T
F	M	H	A	O	D	G	A	Y	E
M	A	S	S	E	U	R	B	E	A
O	I	P	O	G	H	O	O	F	C
S	D	R	N	S	C	O	A	C	H
L	A	V	T	D	U	M	K	I	E
H	B	A	K	E	R	L	W	A	R
N	L	L	H	C	X	F	O	R	T
S	W	E	E	P	G	P	L	M	N
K	O	T	H	I	J	U	D	G	E

1. Maid 2. Mason 3. Masseur 4. Groom
5. Coach 6. Valet 7. Baker 8. Teacher
9. Sweep 10. Judge

Solution 79

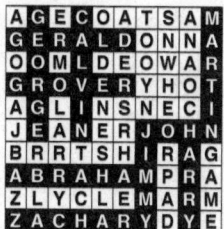

1. Harry 2. Abraham 3. Calvin 4. John
5. Grover 6. Zachary 7. Gerald 8. Martin
9. Jimmy 10. George

Solution 81

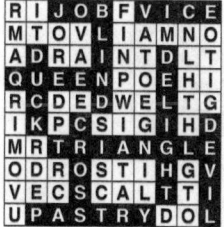

1. Job 2. Blind 3. Duck 4. Queen
5. Cross 6. Triangle 7. Devil 8. Pastry
9. Delight 10. Vice

Solution 83

1. Paris 2. Rome 3. Dublin 4. Madrid
5. Havana 6. Bern 7. Oslo 8. Bonn
9. Riyadh 10. Nairobi

Solution 80

1. Measure 2. Espionage 3. Part
4. Weight 5. Foil 6. Attack 7. Sink 8. Act
9. Pane 10. Tenor

Solution 82

1. Five 2. Chicken 3. Yes 4. Cheese
5. Sun 6. Milk 7. Please 8. Fish
9. Thank you 10. Wine

Solution 84

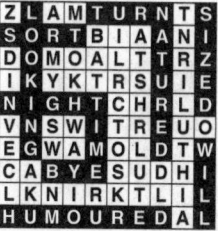

1. Sort 2. Turn 3. Night 4. Bye
5. Humoured 6. Time 7. Looking
8. Natured 9. Sized 10. Will

Solution 85

1. Fowles 2. Scott 3. Greene 4. Kesey
5. Amis 6. Kafka 7. King 8. Wolfe
9. Joyce 10. Carey

Solution 86

1. Franz 2. Roger 3. Johann 4. Pat
5. Gary 6. Paul 7. Peter 8. Tony
9. Bryan 10. Diego

Solution 87

1. Vampire 2. Evil 3. Warlock 4. Goblin
5. Voodoo 6. Ghost 7. Demon 8. Devil
9. Imp 10. Troll

Solution 88

1. Holiday 2. Eye 3. Knock 4. Paradise
5. Nose 6. Land 7. Pie 8. Pet 9. Honour
10. Lift

Solution 89

1. Daniel 2. Dustin 3. Richard 4. Robert
5. Ben 6. Jack 7. Henry 8. Jon 9. Paul
10. Michael

Solution 90

1. Cheese 2. Water 3. Man 4. Thank you
5. House 6. Love 7. Friend 8. Milk
9. Sun 10. No

Solution 91

P	E	T	E	R	T	S	E	M	G
Z	O	B	R	A	H	U	K	I	I
S	U	Z	A	N	N	E	E	C	E
L	L	Y	U	S	T	U	O	H	R
A	R	A	O	M	O	I	R	A	I
B	I	L	L	K	C	T	S	E	W
L	K	P	U	S	A	W	F	L	I
Y	A	U	J	O	H	N	N	A	J
F	O	E	R	L	E	I	K	C	O
T	R	E	V	O	R	O	J	Y	N

1. Peter 2. Suzanne 3. Ulrika 4. Sue
5. Michael 6. John 7. Moira 8. Bill
9. Jon 10. Trevor

Solution 92

S	L	I	L	P	U	P	S	A	C
R	I	S	I	N	G	O	N	L	R
O	L	O	K	C	D	G	T	O	Y
L	Y	H	E	L	P	U	H	W	H
L	M	O	S	M	I	C	D	E	V
I	I	L	G	R	O	L	L	U	O
N	N	D	A	L	L	G	T	X	F
G	O	Q	U	I	S	H	O	T	E
I	H	R	T	E	I	M	U	W	A
T	O	U	C	H	P	O	S	A	W

1. Rising 2. Cry 3. Rolling 4. Help 5. Hold
6. Roll 7. Shot 8. Touch 9. Saw 10. Like

Solution 93

B	V	P	O	L	T	A	I	R	E
E	M	I	I	W	I	L	L	O	W
E	L	N	S	T	E	O	F	C	U
C	H	E	S	T	N	U	T	Y	K
H	C	S	A	D	L	U	S	O	E
S	R	L	I	K	T	R	M	W	O
I	B	I	R	C	H	I	A	L	P
C	T	M	C	M	U	V	P	Y	A
D	I	E	H	U	W	H	L	G	L
Y	E	M	O	A	K	I	E	L	M

1. Beech 2. Pine 3. Chestnut 4. Willow
5. Maple 6. Birch 7. Lime 8. Palm
9. Oak 10. Elm

Solution 94

S	Y	N	R	D	I	C	E	A	T
L	A	B	O	U	R	S	D	O	T
H	N	T	M	Y	M	H	R	T	H
G	T	V	E	L	D	R	E	A	M
R	O	I	O	N	C	E	T	E	V
I	N	A	D	H	O	W	Y	L	W
A	Y	S	L	I	J	E	M	U	E
A	W	W	I	V	E	S	S	O	L
D	N	I	K	T	N	E	L	A	L
O	P	V	E	N	I	C	E	B	V

1. Labours 2. Antony 3. Romeo 4. Dream
5. Shrew 6. Well 7. Ado 8. Like 9. Wives
10. Venice

Solution 95

V	I	M	C	T	H	O	U	S	E
B	R	E	A	K	O	L	A	N	T
A	L	K	S	Z	Y	I	N	R	E
C	H	I	T	S	B	U	R	S	T
K	T	O	R	I	Z	O	U	H	C
L	I	C	R	F	I	E	L	D	D
S	A	O	U	L	W	E	O	A	L
C	L	A	S	S	V	L	O	O	K
R	K	N	T	C	O	A	B	M	R
Y	L	I	R	A	U	W	L	I	T

1. Break 2. Back 3. Cast 4. House
5. Burst 6. Field 7. Look 8. Law
9. Class 10. Cry

Solution 96

Z	O	B	R	B	A	T	E	H	K
P	O	M	C	O	R	C	V	G	R
Y	I	A	N	A	C	O	N	D	A
T	O	M	D	E	O	B	E	K	I
H	U	B	G	L	N	R	O	L	T
O	S	A	I	V	D	A	S	P	C
N	C	H	A	I	T	F	T	U	G
U	T	A	I	P	A	N	I	Y	N
E	X	P	I	E	N	T	H	K	W
T	I	G	E	R	S	N	A	K	E

1. Python 2. Anaconda 3. Boa 4. Mamba
5. Asp 6. Viper 7. Tiger Snake 8. Krait
9. Taipan 10. Cobra

Solution 97

```
E L S A V E R C O D
B U L L A S T A X I
L O O Z E C O P E L
O S W A M O N E Y E
M H A S I M K S U G
P A L I C E N T O R
E P T B E D R A L O
T E Z I A Y O G L U
O M E L D E M E A N
C A N T O T E N R D
```

1. Waltz 2. Mean 3. Money 4. Bull
5. Round 6. Cape 7. Alice 8. Age
9. Taxi 10. Comedy

Solution 98

```
E H O U S E I R S A
Y A A G L I T K T G
E N T E R P R I S E
S D T I M C A H E N
H S T L K O D Z J T
R Z S T Y L E O F L
A U L T R O U G A M
N N A M E W I L L A
G R U P E A E B L I
E M I S L Y V O N I
```

1. Enterprise 2. Agent 3. Hand 4. House
5. Trade 6. Style 7. Fall 8. Will 9. Range
10. Way

Solution 99

```
K A R V I D N I C D
K E I T H D E A T U
N S N L I Z I L C K
D R G I P F K C H E
I D O O E L A H F O
Z I T S T E W A R T
Z C J N E I T R L X
Y J O C L M I L E S
H O H I M T I I U S
B E N N Y R T E O W
```

1. Keith 2. Ringo 3. Duke 4. Charlie
5. Stewart 6. John 7. Miles 8. Benny
9. Pete 10. Dizzy

Solution 100

```
Z G L E A J O B U B
H O R N P I P E T A
A G S I T G R L F L
W O V U L A V L U L
E L C L O G C Y K E
R C Y I O S S H E T
M O R R I S L D D L
W N U A O N J U M I
I G L T X W A L T Z
T A N G O N R I P A
```

1. Hornpipe 2. Go-Go 3. Clog 4. Ballet
5. Belly 6. Jig 7. Morris 8. Conga 9. Waltz
10. Tango

Solution 101

```
F R I M S A M B O T
N O T U Q L I W R U
S S E A U R C H I N
I H A L I L R A L A
G A T X D A N L K O
C R A B T D O E E L
W K P M S G I M P Y
I N O H E R R I N G
N T R I A L K O V E
E M A R L I N Y T N
```

1. Sea Urchin 2. Shark 3. Crab 4. Squid
5. Tuna 6. Whale 7. Eel 8. Seal 9. Marlin
10. Herring

Solution 102

```
H I N P A N Y A M T
E M T A A N Z C T I
R O F N D W E H R C
A T D D T K M I I A
O E R O S I J L S R
J O L R I G U L L U
A T L A S F Z E U S
S F L I T C R S O F
O T I M P O N T L C
N G H E R A C L E S
```

1. Zeus 2. Icarus 3. Eros 4. Atlas 5. Pan
6. Pandora 7. Achilles 8. Jason 9. Hera
10. Heracles

Solution 103

```
F P G I M P O L H T
G A G G L E L I E U
L C W Y O N X D R N
I K A B Z P R I D E
T M I R U M I S C A
S C H O O L M O F L
W O N O F K R I L P
A G E D U T R O O P
R A L A M U I L C I
M R T E A M A G K N
```

1. Gaggle 2. Pack 3. Pride 4. Herd
5. School 6. Swarm 7. Brood 8. Troop
9. Team 10. Flock

Solution 104

```
U L B K L E R L P F
C H E E T A H U N O
D Z A D I G N T O X
H O R L G L I O N W
G R Z H C E Y W T I
I L C Y T E R L D A
T I G E R S V I C N
E E S N L B S D E T
M S H A R K V T Y H
A E U R T Y W O L F
```

1. Cheetah 2. Bear 3. Eagle 4. Fox
5. Lion 6. Owl 7. Tiger 8. Hyena 9. Shark
10. Wolf

Solution 105

```
F L I T C R O G F S
K C H A R L I E T T
H I A J L T R O S A
F T R F I E J R C N
A L O U S V L G Y F
T S L V B I U E X J
T N D L O R O M N E
Y E K D B U S T E R
L M K I O S H Y Y R
W I L L B D A N N Y
```

1. Jerry 2. Stan 3. Buster 4. Bob
5. Danny 6. George 7. Will 8. Charlie
9. Harold 10. Fatty

Solution 106

```
G I C I S L P L U M
C U R R Y H T I F U
H L E D R I A P L S
E P A P P L E T R T
E K M O F F I N R A
S I X O S I A M I R
E J E S O U P W E D
F C M A O R S U L N
H I N L T D I X N Z
M I N T B B R E A D
```

1. Curry 2. Plum 3. Mustard 4. Apple
5. Soup 6. Salt 7. Bread 8. Mint
9. Cheese 10. Cream

Solution 107

```
S F W G M B O S C C
L R I B L J Y E N L
H E R O F W A R V I
X E D D R P E U S M
I Z L Y U S D M E A
N E N N O E F R L X
D M C S G M H Y N X
Y A M K E I R I A I
C H R I S T X S Z W
M I N D P E L R I T
```

1. Hero 2. Freeze 3. Climax 4. Body
5. Serum 6. War 7. Semite 8. Nazi
9. Christ 10. Skid

Solution 108

```
X S L K P R I Z E X
P O N D R W I L J L
B I L L I N G T E G
I L L T O V E F N A
L V F P R K P N S L
T R L L I S D H D L
I C O A T M R A N A
D U O J Y P T T K N
O W R E E L D W L T
G I J N O T C H R P
```

1. Soil 2. Billing 3. Prize 4. Priority
5. Floor 6. Dog 7. Coat 8. Notch 9. Hat
10. Gallant

Solution 109

1. Manfred 2. John 3. Neil 4. Wilbur
5. Charles 6. Louis 7. Ross 8. Amy
9. Yuri 10. Erich

Solution 110

1. Football 2. London 3. Dover 4. Dickens
5. Thames 6. Rain 7. Tea 8. Pub 9. Bitter
10. Rose

Solution 111

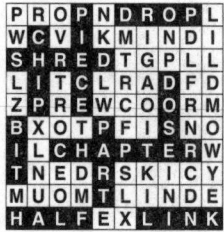

1. Shred 2. Chip 3. Drop 4. Dose 5. Bit
6. Piece 7. Chapter 8. Part 9. Link
10. Half

Solution 112

1. Little 2. Derek 3. Jill 4. French 5. Pace
6. Antony 7. Son 8. Wise 9. Costello
10. Laurel

Solution 113

1. Board 2. Back 3. Crown 4. Wit 5. Term
6. Inch 7. Nelson 8. Hearted 9. Marathon
10. Mast

Solution 114

1. Garden 2. Snake 3. Dove 4. Boot
5. Bass 6. Salmon 7. Cake 8. Horse
9. Salt 10. Chair

Solution 115

```
L J I L T Z H O R N
B O A T F E M I K O
O G R L I N N O U J
W I M W L I F N X O
X W G N H D A Z O H
D I S T A N C E U N
L N T R N A E X E S
P D L I D S M C K E
S E K L K T I M U N
I D L R I F J U M P
```

1. Boat 2. Bow 3. Arm 4. Horn 5. Winded
6. Distance 7. Hand 8. Face 9. Jump
10. Johns

Solution 116

```
S P I D R I M A U W
C A L A I S X L T I
R R I N C E E F U N
G I L B R I E W G E
A S K I Y N X L L F
F M N I C E N N O I
R W U P R L I T U S
A L P S P F A K V T
N S I K L U N I R O
C A N C A N R Y E N
```

1. Calais 2. Seine 3. Brie 4. Wine
5. Louvre 6. Cancan 7. Nice 8. Franc
9. Alps 10. Paris

Solution 117

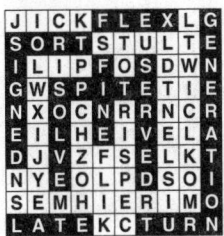

```
G K W I L F K O F K
K A F K A G N K E I
Y R I X L K L E I N
E L D K I R S R X N
K O R B U T L R K O
A F E S J K I T I C
M F P K E L L Y R K
R P K I L O U T K F
K H A N I N D R L K
T D L G M K E A T S
```

1. Korbut 2. Karloff 3. Kafka 4. Klein
5. King 6. Kelly 7. Kinnock 8. Kerr
9. Keats 10. Khan

Solution 118

```
T Y I C R U L M A Y
R A C R F O D P L I
A M N E S T Y V I L
R B Z A E X N W O A
M I C M N J A M M Y
Y Q U Y L D M L D M
F S T D N I O R I A
M A R R Y K G S K N
R Q O N M J I H L H
P Y J A M A S L C G
```

1. Army 2. Amnesty 3. Yam 4. Dynamo
5. Creamy 6. Jammy 7. Layman 8. Marry
9. May 10. Pyjamas

Solution 119

```
J I C K F L E X L G
S O R T S T U L T E
I L I P F O S D W N
G W S P I T E T I E
N X O C N R R N C R
E I L H E I V E L A
D J V Z F S E L K T
N Y E O L P D S O I
S E M H I E R I M O
L A T E K C T U R N
```

1. Signed 2. Sort 3. Fine 4. Flex
5. Generation 6. Served 7. Spite 8. Solve
9. Turn 10. Late

Solution 120

```
X F O R M A N V O S
R O M E P R A W U T
E S P D E M M E S O
S S L F I N R L L N
P E K O M L T L Y E
C L N R N A U E N U
F O R D X N H S D L
T J E U L G W R O E
W O N M R M T I L A
I V E K H U S T O N
```

1. Forman 2. Stone 3. Demme 4. Welles
5. Redford 6. Ford 7. Lean 8. Huston
9. Lang 10. Fosse